GORDON KORMAN
I WANT TO GO HOME!

Other books by Gordon Korman

Beware the Fish!
Go Jump in the Pool!
This Can't Be Happening at Macdonald Hall!
The War with Mr. Wizzle

**More APPLE PAPERBACKS
you will want to read:**

*Encyclopedia Brown and the Case
of the Dead Eagles*
   by Donald J. Sobol
Encyclopedia Brown Carries On
   by Donald J. Sobol
Encyclopedia Brown Solves Them All
   by Donald J. Sobol
The Magic Moscow
   by Daniel Pinkwater
*The Revenge of the Incredible Dr. Rancid
and His Youthful Assistant, Jeffrey*
   by Ellen Conford
Son for a Day
   by Corinne Gerson

GORDON KORMAN
I WANT TO GO HOME!

AN
APPLE
PAPERBACK

SCHOLASTIC INC.
New York Toronto London Auckland Sydney

ISBN 0-590-44111-6

12 11 10 9 8 7 6 5 4 3 2 1   0 1 2 3 4 5/9

Printed in the U.S.A.   28

There's fun, and then there's fun.
This book is dedicated to those
who know the difference.

Contents

1
Cabin 13

The early summer sunshine streamed down over Camp Algonkian Island. The trim on the twenty-two cabins was brightly painted, the excellent athletic fields had been freshly mowed, and an assortment of boats of all sizes bobbed in readiness at the dock. The campers would begin arriving right after lunch. Everything was prepared for the opening of the camp's thirty-first season.

A shaft of light came through the window of the camp office, shining directly upon the solemn portrait of Elias Warden, the camp founder, and glaring off the glass. The present camp director, Arthur Warden, grandson of Elias, sat at his desk, checking the final preparations for the new camp year. There was a record enrolment for this first month, he noted with satisfaction. How lovely that would look on the bank statement!

He noticed a letter on the corner of his desk, opened it and examined the contents.

Dear Mr. Warden, it read, *we are writing this letter in regard to our son, Rudy Miller, who is registered at your camp for the first month. We thought that perhaps you and your counsellors should be forewarned. Rudy is an exceptional but difficult boy. You may have considerable problems getting him adjusted to camp life. He is something of a loner, and does not always get on well with other boys. In addition, he insists that he does not want to go to camp. However, we are sending him to Algonkian Island on the advice of his school guidance department. They feel that he must be placed in a social atmosphere where he will be exposed to all sorts of people, an atmosphere of hearty physical activity mixed with healthy comradeship.*

Mr. Warden looked up. "What an excellent description of camp!" he said aloud.

When Rudy arrives, the letter went on, *it is very likely that he will have a rather negative attitude. It is our sincere hope that you and your staff will be patient with him. Please inform us if you have any problems. Sincerely yours, Mr. and Mrs. Edward Miller.*

Mr. Warden snorted loudly. "Problems! There is no such thing as a problem boy—only problem parents. All cats love meat, and all boys love camp. That's the way it was in the days of my grandfather—that's the way it is now. This boy is about to have the best summer of his life!" He got up from his desk, strode out onto his front porch and looked out over the compound, still holding the letter.

A group of tall, strong young men, dressed alike in white Algonkian uniforms, were moving about putting the finishing touches on the grounds in preparation for the arrival of their charges.

Frank, the head counsellor, loped over to Mr. Warden's cottage. "Good morning, sir. We're all set here.

Are there any last minute problems we should know about?"

Mr. Warden glanced briefly towards the letter in his hand, crumpled it up and tossed it into the nearest trash container. "Never any problems at Algonkian Island. Just routine, my boy, just routine."

He turned away and walked briskly back into his office. By the time he was again seated at his desk, Rudy Miller had completely vanished from his mind.

* * *

The large silver motor launch chugged loudly up to the island dock and scraped against the old tires that covered the wood. The driver skilfully threw a rope around a post and secured the boat.

He turned to his nine young passengers. "Well, we're here, kids. Camp Algonkian Island. Everybody out."

There was scrambling and happy chatter as eight of the boys heaved themselves and their luggage out of the launch. Once on the dock they scattered, heading for the assorted small buildings on the island. There were welcoming shouts as boys already there ran to greet the new arrivals.

The driver glanced at the lone passenger still seated at the rear of the launch. "Hey, what are you, asleep or something? We're here."

"So I see," the dark-haired boy observed glumly. He did not move.

"Well?" prompted the driver. "Aren't you getting out?"

"No," said the boy blandly. "I'm hoping you won't

notice me so I can hitch a ride back to civilization."

"Aw, c'mon," kidded the driver. "You're going to have a great time here."

"I doubt it," said the boy, heaving his duffle bag onto the dock and climbing out after it. "But thanks for the thought."

Rudy Miller watched regretfully as the motor launch pulled away from the dock and headed for the mainland. There went his last link with the outside world. Like it or not—and he did not like it—Camp Algonkian Island was home for the next month.

"You'll love it, dear," his mother had assured him at the bus station earlier that day. "The sports facilities are the best available. And there will be so many other boys your own age to play with."

Well, the latter was certainly true, at least. He had come up on the bus and over on the launch with eight others, and there were hundreds more swarming all over what he could see of the island, every one obviously delighted to be here. Rudy abandoned all attempts to understand such an attitude. He was here thanks to the school guidance department. Thanks, but no thanks. Guidance should stick to timetabling and stay out of other people's heads!

An athletic young man with a clipboard loped up and grinned into Rudy's face. "Ah, here you are, the ninth guy from the launch. You must be Miller."

Rudy nodded noncommittally.

"Hi. I'm Dave, the swimming coach. You're in Cabin 13, right over there." He indicated the row of small, wood-frame buildings which lined the camp's central compound.

"Thirteen," repeated Rudy softly. "Marvellous."

"You're new here, eh?" said Dave brightly. "This is your first summer at Algonkian?"

Rudy nodded. "And hopefully my last."

Dave stared at him momentarily, then went on. "I'm making up my life-saving class. What level of swimming are you at?"

Rudy thought carefully. "What comes before tadpole?"

"Before tadpole?" the instructor repeated. "Non-swimmer . . . oh, well, we'll have you swimming soon enough. By the time this month is over you'll be a regular ocean-going vessel."

"I doubt it," said Rudy calmly. He slung his duffle bag over his shoulder and walked across the compound along one of the many well-worn paths, this one leading to Cabin 13.

Standing in the doorway was another athletic-looking young man, dressed like Dave in an Algonkian T-shirt, shorts, white socks and track shoes, and sporting a whistle around his neck. On his face was Dave's elaborate grin. Rudy looked back at Dave and then again at the counsellor of Cabin 13. A clone, he decided. There were two of them.

"Hi, there!" the clone greeted him with a hearty slap on the back. "I'm Chip, your bunk counsellor. What's your name?"

"Just put me down as Anonymous," said Rudy.

Undaunted, Chip glanced at the tag on the duffle bag. "Rudy Miller. Welcome aboard, Miller. You're the first to arrive. You've got the pick of the bunks."

Rudy stepped inside and looked around with distaste.

There were three double-decker bunk beds in a line

on each side of the room, and a small private bedroom at the front, just inside the door. Rudy went into the private room and sat down on the bed.

"I'll have this one," he decided.

"Oh, no," said Chip seriously. "This is the counsellor's room. I sleep here. But you can have your pick of all the others."

"Not much privacy out there," Rudy remarked mildly.

"Hey, you don't need privacy! We're all going to be one big happy family, and we're going to have lots of fun!"

Rudy glared at him, shook his head resignedly and walked out of the small room. Once again he surveyed the bunks, and selecting the lower bed in one of the far corners, stuffed his duffle underneath and threw himself down on the thin mattress.

"That's right," Chip said approvingly. "You just make yourself comfortable. I'm going to stand outside and greet the rest of the guys." He stepped out the front door.

Rudy looked around thoughtfully. Soon the other bunks would be occupied and the room would be burgeoning with bodies. He stood up and pulled the sheets off the bunk directly above him. Then, stuffing the ends in under the upper mattress, he let the sheets fall to the floor, completely draping his own bed off from the rest of the room. He crawled inside, dragging his duffle bag with him. Behind the sheet there was a flurry of activity. Then a hand appeared and affixed a neatly-lettered sign to the drape by means of a sticky bandaid. It read: *DO NOT DISTURB*.

Ah, he thought, lying down in seclusion, privacy.

Pulling a Sony walkman out of the duffle, he placed the earphones over his ears and set the volume to maximum.

* * *

Mike Webster trudged slowly along the pathway to Cabin 13, his new suitcase dragging at his hand and his guitar slung over his bony shoulder. The sun was too hot. He felt as though his pale skin was burning already. Camp, he reflected, was everything he had expected it to be—big, strange, isolated and generally rotten. If this was his parents' idea of a reward for getting top marks in school, he thanked his lucky stars that he hadn't flunked. That probably would have meant the rack. As it was, he had been banished to this island camp for a whole month. Four weeks of nothing but sports! What a depressing thought!

From inside the cabin he could hear excited chatter. Grimly, he entered. Several boys were gathered at the rear, surrounding a bunk which was shut off from the rest of the room by drapes.

"Don't tell me," blurted Mike. "We're quarantined with mumps!"

One of the boys turned to face him. "No, it's probably just a nut."

"Probably?" asked Mike. "Don't you know?"

"I'm not poking around in there," said another boy. "Look at the sign."

Mike read the sign. "Is there anybody in there?"

"Who knows?" shrugged a tall boy. "My bunk is up front. Why should I worry about it?"

With a sinking heart, Mike looked around. All the bunks were occupied except—except for the one right above the mysterious nut. Zonked again. Camp was getting worse by the minute. Cautiously he climbed up the small wooden ladder and looked at his bed.

"Hey, there are no sheets up here!"

"Tough," came a muffled voice from below.

"There *is* someone in there," whispered one of the boys.

"Are those my sheets?" Mike demanded of the hidden presence.

"They came from up there," said the voice.

"Well, this is where I have to sleep!" shouted Mike.

Chip came bounding into the cabin. "What's going on in here? What's all the yelling about?" He stopped short at the sight of the draped bunk. "Miller, is that you in there?" He ripped the sheets down, revealing Rudy and his transistor radio.

Rudy turned off the radio. "I just wanted a little privacy," he said quietly.

"Nobody comes to camp for privacy," said Chip brightly.

"Only because they can't get any," Rudy replied. He turned over and switched the radio back on. "Wake me up in a month."

Chip stared at him for a moment and then turned to Mike. "Hi. I didn't catch you on the way in. What's your name?"

"Mike Webster," Mike replied without much enthusiasm.

"Welcome aboard. I'm Chip, your counsellor." He gestured to the rest of the boys. "Obviously Miller's a little homesick," he said in a low voice. "We'll all have to do our best to make him feel at home."

"He's a nut," said Harold Greene, a short blond boy. "Why did our cabin have to get stuck with a nut?"

"Knock it off!" said Chip. "He's just homesick. He'll come around once we get into the activities. Here, Webster, I'll help you make up your bunk."

* * *

The boys from Cabin 13, sweaty and tired from playing baseball, came laughing and shouting into their cabin to change for dinner.

"Well, we lost," said Chip brightly, "but we had more fun than they did."

"Sure," laughed someone. "They're exhausted from all that base-running!"

"Wow!" exclaimed Harold Greene, pulling off his sweat socks. "Thirty-seven to nothing!"

"A no-hitter," moaned Adam Willis, a tall boy with red hair.

"That was some sacrifice bunt you hit, Webster," exclaimed Chip with forced enthusiasm. "Too bad there was nobody on base or we would really have showed them something!"

Mike smiled thinly. "Thanks." He had always hated baseball. His "bunt" had been the result of the hardest swing he could manage.

"Congratulations," muttered a low voice sarcastically.

Everybody turned. They had forgotten Rudy, who was still lying on his bunk listening to his walkman.

"Ah, Miller," said Chip brightly. "We missed you out there. You'll play next time."

"I doubt it," said Rudy softly. "I don't play baseball."

"Well," said Chip, still smiling, "dinner's in ten minutes."

"You *do* eat, don't you?" put in Harold.

Rudy cast him a withering glare.

* * *

The mess hall was crowded and noisy. Rudy had tried to find a secluded spot to eat his dinner, but there was no such thing. Each cabin had its own table with its own clone to watch over things. There wasn't even any elbow room. He had been directed to carry his tray to table 13—that number again!—and now he found himself sitting on a hard bench right next to Mike Webster.

"Hi," said Mike timidly.

Rudy acknowledged this greeting with a curt nod, then shook his head and took a bite of his dinner. He chewed thoughtfully, swallowed and put down his fork.

He said, "What is this material?"

"It's beef stew," mumbled Chip, his mouth full to overflowing. "Isn't it great?"

"No," said Rudy flatly.

"Oh, well, you just don't have much of an appetite because you didn't play baseball," the counsellor explained. "Isn't it delicious, Webster?"

Mike looked sadly at his plate. "Yeah, great," he muttered. He had not even ventured to taste it yet. Maybe it was true that a person could fast for almost a month at a time.

Rudy stood up and lifted his plate. "Since you like it so much," he said mildly, "have mine." He delicately scraped all his stew onto Mike's plate.

"Miller, leave the table!" ordered Chip.

"Certainly," said Rudy. He climbed over the bench

and walked out of the mess hall.

"What a nut!" exclaimed Harold.

"Yeah," agreed Joey Peters, a small, dark boy. "Why did we get stuck with him?"

"He's just homesick," Chip maintained. "He'll come around as soon as he realizes the fun he's missing. Just let him be."

"I'm not going near him," Harold promised. "He's a nut!"

* * *

"Okay, lights out," announced Chip. "Because it's the first night and you're all excited, you don't have to go right to sleep. I'll be at a counsellors' meeting for an hour or so. Just keep it down to a low roar." He left.

Instantly the boys began chattering amongst themselves. Mike Webster climbed up to his bunk and lay down, trying not to think of real food. He felt a kick from below.

"Do you have to hang there like that?" asked Rudy in annoyance.

Mike sat up, pulled his guitar out of its case and began to strum absently.

"Oh, no," groaned Rudy's voice. "Music."

"What's wrong with music?" Mike demanded.

"With music, nothing; with *that*, plenty."

"It's a free country!"

"I wish it was," sighed Rudy. He rolled over resignedly and went to sleep.

2
In the garbage

At the first sound of the bugle playing reveille, Rudy Miller jumped up and smashed his head on the upper bunk. Mike Webster, also shocked awake, came tumbling down and hit the floor with a resounding thud. The other boys, completely unperturbed, began to rouse themselves slowly.

"What—" moaned Rudy.

The door flew open and Chip bounded into the room, already dressed. "All right, you guys, rise and shine! It's a beautiful day here at Algonkian!"

"Algonkian, my foot," mumbled Rudy. "This is Alcatraz." He reached into his duffle, produced a piece of chalk and drew a small line on the cabin wall beside his bed. "One," he counted miserably.

"One what?" asked Mike, picking himself painfully up off the floor.

"One day gone," Rudy explained. "Only twenty-seven more to go."

"Hey!" exclaimed Mike. "It's only six o'clock!"

"Of course," said Chip. "Early to bed, early to rise."

"Yes," said Rudy. "Makes a man healthy, wealthy and dead. I'm going to get a few more hours sleep."

"Miller, you get out of that bed!" hollered Chip. "We've got breakfast, and then the camp director's going to speak to all of us. Get moving!"

"Alcatraz," Rudy repeated, rummaging in his bag for some clothes.

The boys got dressed and Chip marched them over to the wash station, which was located at a point central to their group of cabins. Rudy and Mike found themselves side by side at the sinks brushing their teeth. Awkwardly, they eyed each other.

"Truce?" Mike suggested shyly.

Rudy shrugged.

"I'm sorry about the music," ventured Mike.

"I've heard worse," admitted Rudy generously.

Mike was surprised. As far as he knew, this was the first civil word Rudy had spoken to anyone. Mike returned to the business of brushing his teeth, but kept a curious eye on his peculiar bunkmate.

"*Breakfast!*" bellowed Chip. From the wash station he led Cabin 13 to the mess hall.

As they stood in line with their trays, Mike and Rudy, still side by side, continued to eye each other curiously.

"I don't suppose they can really ruin breakfast," suggested Mike hopefully.

"I have faith," said Rudy quietly.

The two boys chose their breakfast and sat down at table 13.

"Well, Miller," Chip greeted him, "you'd better eat a hearty breakfast because today we're going to have relay races."

"Are you?" said Rudy mildly. He assumed a long-suffering look. "It's a shame I'll have to miss that."

"Why?" asked the counsellor.

"I don't run," Rudy explained.

"He doesn't do anything!" exclaimed Harold Greene.

"Exactly," Rudy agreed.

"How do you do that?" Mike whispered. "How do you get out of doing all those crummy camp things?"

"It's very simple. You just don't go."

Mike looked at him with something like admiration in his eyes.

"Eat up, everybody," called Chip, "because we have the assembly with the camp director in ten minutes. When you've returned your tray, go out to the ball field."

"Miller won't be coming," announced Harold Greene sarcastically. "All he does is listen to the radio."

Rudy stood up, picked up his tray and started towards the tray-return conveyor belt. As he passed the end of the table, he carefully tilted the tray, sending the remains of his breakfast—corn flakes and milk, scrambled eggs and orange juice—sliding off into Harold's lap.

"Oops," he said mildly.

A high-pitched giggle escaped Mike Webster.

"Miller," stormed Chip, "you did that on purpose!"

"He did that on purpose!" echoed Harold, outraged.

"It does look that way," Rudy admitted.

"That'll cost you two days work detail!" exclaimed Chip.

"Darn it," said Rudy, "I thought I was going to get solitary confinement."

"And clean that up!" Chip ranted. "Greene, go and

change. Hurry up, you guys. We can't keep the camp director waiting."

* * *

The entire population of Camp Algonkian Island was assembled on the baseball diamond in front of a hastily erected podium. Frank, the head counsellor, dressed in shorts and T-shirt exactly like Chip and his counterparts, walked up to the microphone and addressed the group.

"Hi, gang! Are we having a great time?"

"Do we want an honest answer?" muttered Rudy.

Mike snickered.

Both were drowned out by the loud cheering from almost three hundred throats.

"I know you're all anxious to get into the fun," the head counsellor went on, "but first, let's give a nice warm Algonkian welcome to our camp director, Mr. Warden!"

"How appropriate," murmured Rudy, nodding wisely. "A Warden for Alcatraz."

Mike laughed out loud.

"Shhh!" said Chip warningly. "Webster, behave yourself!"

As the applause died down, Mr. Warden, a short, bald, middle-aged man with skinny bow legs sticking out of Bermuda shorts, stepped up to the microphone.

"Good morning, boys," he greeted the assembly. "It gives me great pleasure to welcome you to Algonkian."

"It would give me great pleasure to go home," mumbled Rudy.

Mike snorted loudly into the silence.

"Webster!"

"This is Camp Algonkian Island," Mr. Warden continued. "It was founded thirty-one years ago by my grandfather, Elias Warden. I like to think of Algonkian as the finest camp in Ontario. We have facilities for every activity you can think of. Camp is a great experience for a young man. Aside from the obvious advantage of enjoyment, a camper grows up with clear eyes, strong back and straight limbs."

"Obviously," murmured Rudy, "*you* didn't get to go to camp."

Mike looked at Mr. Warden's skinny bow legs, and the whole thing proved too much for him. It began in his throat, progressed to a series of muffled giggles, and rose to a mighty crescendo.

"Webster!" exclaimed a horrified Chip. "What's wrong with you?"

By now everyone except Mr. Warden was devoting full attention to Mike's display. The director was still rambling on about the benefits of camp.

"Webster, stop it!"

But there was no stopping it. Mike was doubled over in agony, vainly trying to suppress his wild laughter. His merriment was infectious. One by one, other boys began to laugh. Soon the whole island was rocking with hysteria.

"Webster!" shouted Chip over the din. "You caused all this! Two days work detail for you!"

Meanwhile, Mr. Warden was delighted with the wonderful reception the boys were giving him. This was going to be the best summer yet. What an ovation!

Chip held his head. Between Webster and Miller, he was going to have his hands full for the next four weeks.

* * *

Pushing a large red wheelbarrow loaded to overflowing with green garbage bags, Mike started up the wooded path to the dump. He sighed heavily. Work detail. His first full day at camp and already he was in the garbage. What a fun place.

A few boys gathering wood for the evening bonfire grinned sympathetically as he struggled past. The front wheel struck the exposed root of an old tree and one of the bags rolled out of the barrow and broke open. Chicken bones were everywhere. Mike looked hopelessly at the evening sky as if for a sign. None came. Oh well, at least now he knew why they had equipped him with a shovel. After scooping up the mess, he continued down the path. He could see the dump now —and smell it too. He wrinkled his nose as he trudged up to the mound, then stopped short. There, flat on his back in his wheelbarrow, lay Rudy Miller. His portable radio was in his hand, the jack was in his ear, and his eyes were closed. His normally expressionless face wore a blissful look.

Self-consciously, Mike silently dumped his cargo. After all, what could he say or do? Miller had given every indication that his only desire was to be left alone. Mike couldn't very well declare himself a friend. But wouldn't it be great! Miller was the only person who hated camp as much as he did!

"Hi," he ventured finally.

Rudy gave no indication of having heard him.

Mike shrugged. Oh well, if he doesn't want anything to do with me, then the feeling is mutual, he thought. He started to pilot his wheelbarrow back in the direction of the camp.

"Hey," said a voice from behind him, "I suppose you're blaming me for getting you put on the garbage squad."

Mike wheeled to face Rudy, who had pocketed his radio and was sitting up. "Of course not—yes! Yes, I *am* blaming you. You made me laugh!"

"I was talking to myself," Rudy protested. "You were eavesdropping."

"Whatever," said Mike wearily, just to avoid an argument.

Rudy climbed out of his wheelbarrow and sat down on a rock. Mike sat on the ground facing him.

"Camp!" Rudy said with malice in his voice. "Alcatraz, a Warden, clones —and now garbage!"

"I'm here as a reward," said Mike unhappily. "Good marks in school."

Rudy nodded understandingly. "I'm here on a guidance rap. The school guidance department misguided my parents into guiding me here. They're going to make a well-adjusted, social animal out of me. They think."

"You don't like it here very much, do you?"

"It shows, does it?"

Mike had to laugh. "Well, in case you hadn't noticed, I'm not too thrilled with camp either."

"I noticed," confirmed Rudy.

"It's getting pretty dark," observed Mike. "I guess we'd better be getting back."

"Why? So we can sit around their stupid campfire

and howl at the moon? I'd like to set fire to the whole place, starting with the Warden's house. *That* would be a fire I could sing around!"

Mike looked at him uncertainly. "But you wouldn't do anything like that, would you?"

"Oh, no, of course not. It was just a pleasant thought."

Both boys lapsed into silence, listening to the gurgling of the nearby creek.

Rudy scratched his head thoughtfully. "You know," he began slowly, "if a natural disaster occurred, making the camp unlivable, they'd have to send us home."

Mike nodded his agreement. "It's a shame we don't have many natural disasters around here."

"But what if it was a man-made natural disaster?" Rudy insisted. "What if, for instance, that creek was dammed up and re-routed towards the cabins? Nobody would get hurt, but we'd be up to our ears in mud. The cabin floors would be wet and the insects would be really terrible. They'd definitely have to send us home."

"It sounds great," said Mike mournfully, "but we could never do it."

"Speak for yourself," said Rudy. "I'm starting tomorrow." The sound of singing voices swelled on the evening breeze. "Okay, let's go back now. But first, do you want to help me pick out a few choice bits of garbage?"

"What for?"

"Harold Greene's shoes," Rudy explained. "I've noticed there's usually nothing in them but feet."

Mike laughed appreciatively. "Sure." He picked up an orange peel. "How about this?"

"Admirable," replied Rudy. "You're not bad, you know. You'll do."

Mike laughed again. "Now that I'll do, maybe you'll tell me your name. All I know is '*Miller!*' " He did a creditable imitation of Chip's angry cry.

"That's me. Rudy Miller."

"Hi. I'm Mike Webster."

The two let down the handles of their wheelbarrows and shook hands solemnly. Then, side by side, they moved off in the direction of the campsite.

Near the deserted dump, the creek gurgled on.

3
Dear Mom and Dad

"Hey!" howled Harold Greene early the next morning. "My shoes, there's something in my shoes! Someone put something in my shoes! Miller put something in my shoes! Chip! Chip!"

Chip came bounding onto the scene. "What's going on around here? What's all the yelling about?"

Harold held up one of his dripping running shoes. "Look at this! Look what Miller did!"

"*Miller!*" bellowed the counsellor. "What is this?"

Rudy took the running shoe and examined it carefully. "Garbage," he diagnosed. "More specifically, an eggshell, an orange peel and some unidentified slop, obviously from the mess hall."

"All right, Miller," said Chip angrily, "you'll wash these sneakers!"

"Why do you immediately assume that I'm guilty?" asked Rudy in a hurt tone.

Chip was taken aback. "Well—did you do it?"

"Yes."

"Then spill that stuff out and take the shoes over to the laundry, you hear me?"

Rudy nodded. "They can probably hear you on the mainland."

"All right, you guys," called Chip, "hurry up and get dressed and go to breakfast. This morning we write letters home. Meet back here at the cabin after chow."

"I'll be interested to see what Miller writes home," said Harold Greene savagely. "I've never seen a letter written by a nut before."

"Shut up!" snapped Mike Webster.

"That's enough!" bellowed Chip. "Get moving!"

Rudy reached over and chalked another line on the wall beside his bed. "Two," he counted.

"Only twenty-six more," sighed Mike.

"Barring any natural disaster," Rudy added, poker-faced.

Chip was herding the other boys out the door. "Miller, Webster, hurry! You two catch up with us at the wash station."

Rudy reached over and picked up Harold Greene's pillow. "Would you please hold this pillowcase open?" he said to Mike.

"What are you doing?"

"Clone's orders," said Rudy righteously. "I was told to spill the garbage out of Harold's running shoes."

"Yeah," said Mike, "but in his pillow . . . ?"

"No one said just where. I thought this was as good a place as any."

"You'll get into trouble," warned Mike.

"So I'll get another work detail and I'll haul a little more garbage. Anyway, the dump is the only place on Alcatraz where a guy can get any privacy."

"Oh, all right," laughed Mike, holding open the pillowcase and watching the garbage drop inside. "Little Harold has a big mouth that needs shutting."

"Precisely," Rudy agreed.

* * *

Dear Mom and Dad, wrote Rudy. *This place is terrible. Each day I am subjected to countless atrocities. The food is spoiled and poisonous, and the drinking water is contaminated so there is an outbreak of typhoid. Our cabin collapsed last night in a typhoon, but don't worry. Only one guy got killed.*

It's not all bad. I do have one friend, named Mike. He's the one who pulled me out of the quicksand. I have to haul garbage every day, but there aren't too many wild animals at the dump and I've only been bitten twice.

Mr. Warden, the director, is very nice, and he has a real social conscience. He hires only desperate criminals as counsellors. Our bunk counsellor, whose name is Chip, is a reformed axe-murderer on parole. He has red eyes and yells a lot and keeps an axe under his mattress.

Tonight is really going to be fun. Our cabin hasn't been fixed yet, so we get to sleep in trees. I sure hope the typhoon doesn't start up again.

I'll be safe and sound so long as Algonkian Island doesn't sink any further.

Your son,

Rudy

P.S. If this letter looks messy it's because I'm writing it while being chased by a bear.

Hovering over his letter-writing charges, Chip

stopped beside Rudy's bunk and let out a bellow of rage.

"Miller, what is this?" He ripped the letter out of Rudy's hand. "Typhoid? There's no typhoid here. And no atrocities." He read on. "A typhoon? Are you crazy? ... Criminals? I'm *not* an axe-murderer! I've never even wanted to kill anybody—until now! ... You don't have to sleep in a tree. Nothing happened to the cabin ... Bears? There aren't any bears on the whole island. Miller, you tear this up and write a proper letter!"

"Are you interfering with Her Majesty's mail?" asked Rudy.

"Look, Miller," pleaded Chip, "this stuff is all lies! It'll upset your folks."

"No, it won't," said Rudy. "They don't get upset that easily. They know me."

"Listen," said Chip in exasperation, grabbing Harold Greene's letter from his hand. "This is what a letter is supposed to sound like. *Dear Mom. I'd be having a great time if it weren't for this real nut in our* ... " The counsellor's voice trailed off. "Well, this, then—" He grabbed another letter. "*Dear Mom and Dad. Having a great time. The weather is good. Don't forget to feed my chameleon. Send money. Love, Adam.*" His eyes shone triumphantly. "Now that's a real letter!"

"Mine is more creative," objected Rudy.

"You're going to *mail* that?" cried Chip. "You can't send that! I'll kill you!"

"Threats of violence," said Rudy, making notes.

"Miller," said Chip in a lower tone, "listen to reason. Tear up that letter. Don't you realize the camp could sue you for all those lies?"

Rudy obligingly tore up his masterpiece and sat down to write another.

"Attaboy. You write your folks a nice letter. They deserve it. They're spending a lot of money to send you here."

"And here I thought I was doing time," said Rudy mildly. "How's this?"

Chip took the letter and read it: "*Dear Mom and Dad. How are you? I am okay. This certainly is a camp, all right. Only twelve more days to visting day. Your son, Rudy.* There, now. That's much better," he said with a dubious frown. "Okay, everybody, finish up those letters! We're going to run the obstacle course and we're going to win!"

"Miller won't," sneered Harold Greene.

"Miller certainly won't," agreed Rudy.

"*Why?*" bawled Chip. "You need the exercise and excitement."

"You know I don't run," said Rudy. "Besides, Mike and I are going to arts and crafts."

"We are?" whispered Mike.

"Aw no," protested Chip. "You can do that kind of stuff when it rains."

"It's raining," said Rudy firmly.

"What do you mean, raining? The sun's shining."

"It doesn't have to be raining to be raining."

Chip scratched his head for a moment. Then, "What about you, Webster?" he asked, undaunted. "Why don't you come along and have some fun with us?"

"No, thanks," said Mike, shuffling uncomfortably.

"Oh, let them go," said Harold in disgust. "They'd only ruin everything anyway."

"Greene, you've got a big mouth!" said Chip.

"Agreed," said Rudy.

"You too, Miller!" snapped the counsellor. "Let's go, guys. We're due on the obstacle course. Miller, Webster, we'll see you two at lunch." And he jogged off with the rest of the boys trailing along behind him.

"What do you want to go to arts and crafts for?" asked Mike, mystified.

"We're not going to arts and crafts," Rudy explained. "We're going to build a dam."

A slow smile of understanding spread over Mike's face.

* * *

"What the heck happened to Miller and Webster?" asked Chip, looking around the dining room. "They're twenty minutes late for lunch."

"They're probably finger-painting," sneered Harold. "Or basket-weaving. Isn't that what they always do with nuts?"

"Shut up, Greene," said Chip, standing. "I'm going to find them."

As if on cue, Rudy and Mike walked in the door, two blobs of mud. With every step they took they rained filth down onto the clean wood floor.

"Miller!" cried Chip in horror. "What happened to you guys?"

"It gets a little messy in arts and crafts," offered Rudy.

"What are you building? A dam?"

Mike started visibly. "How did you know?" he blurted.

"Don't get smart, Webster!" snapped Chip. "That'll

cost you another day's work detail. I asked you what you're building."

"A *saleté*," Rudy replied. "A good one."

Chip's face went blank. "A *saleté*—uh, that's nice. All right, you guys, go clean up and grab some lunch. Make it fast because we're going swimming later.

"Well," said Rudy, "Mike and I thought we'd go back and do some more work on our *saleté*."

"But you have to pass the swimming test," protested Chip. "If you don't get your badge you won't be allowed to go canoeing or water-skiing."

"I think I can live with that," Rudy decided. He turned to Mike. "You?"

Mike nodded sheepishly. "I'd rather go back to arts and crafts."

Chip looked pained. "All right. Just for today. Now go and get cleaned up."

On their way to the wash station Mike turned to his companion. "Rudy, what on earth is a *saleté*?"

Although he did not smile, Rudy's poker face assumed an expression of deep satisfaction. "It's French," he explained. "It means dirt."

For the next ten minutes the wash station rang with Mike's laughter.

* * *

Mike waded through the hip-deep muddy water of the creek and heaved himself up onto the grassy bank where he lay panting.

"Rudy, it can't be done. It just can't!"

Rudy surfaced and spat a stream of water in a long arc.

"This is impossible," he gasped, clambering up to join Mike on the grass. "The water must be over a metre deep in the centre."

"There isn't enough brush and mud on this whole island to dam that up," said Mike. "It can't be done!" he repeated.

"Oh, yes it can," said Rudy. "But it would take months. And I'm planning to be out of here long before one month."

"How?" asked Mike. "We just decided we can't dam up this dumb creek."

"My new idea is simplicity itself. We just take off, that's all."

"Great," said Mike sarcastically. "One day we just pick up and walk away. I suppose it never occurred to you that this miserable place is an island."

"We take a boat," Rudy explained patiently.

"That's stealing!"

"No, it isn't. When we're through with it we'll set it afloat back to camp with a note explaining the situation—which is, we're going home."

"Rudy, that's crazy," argued Mike. "Even if we do get across the lake, we're still nowhere. It's two hundred odd kilometres to Toronto!"

"Look," said Rudy, "our resident clone won't let me write to my parents the way I want to, and the Warden sure won't let me use the phone to call them to come and get me. The only way is to get off this rock and get to a phone on the mainland."

"We don't even know where the nearest town is," protested Mike.

"We'll find it. How far can it be? Alcatraz must get its supplies from somewhere close by."

"What about our parents? When the Warden informs them we're missing they'll go nuts!"

Rudy shook his head. "If we leave early enough we'll have phoned home long before His Cloneship even knows we're not in camp." He paused. "Anyway, suit yourself. I'm going tomorrow."

Mike pictured himself at Algonkian without Rudy to talk to. "I'll go," he said quickly.

"All right. Tomorrow before dawn we borrow a motor boat and we're off."

"I guess so," agreed Mike unhappily.

The two sopping, muddy figures began to walk in the direction of the compound.

A pair of beady little eyes watched them go. When the intruders had disappeared, he came out of the underbrush, a lone beaver. His lodge and dam at the far end of the lake had been destroyed by cottage builders. For nearly three weeks he had been searching the lake for a site suitable for a new home, and here was a dam already started . . .

*   *   *

"Hey!" shouted Harold Greene at lights-out. "My pillow—there's something in my pillow! Someone put something in my pillow! Miller put something in my pillow! Chip! *Chip*!"

Chip burst onto the scene. "What's all the yelling about?"

"Miller put garbage in my pillow!"

"*Miller!*" howled Chip, waving the soiled pillow-case. "Did you do this?"

"I would be the logical suspect," admitted Rudy.

"You'll sleep without a pillow for this! Go hang Greene's pillow out on the line to air and give him yours! And another day's work detail for you!"

"I'm not having fun," warned Rudy.

"You'll start having fun when you join in the activities and stop making trouble," growled Chip. He turned to the rest of the group, all in their beds. "Now you guys go to sleep right away. I've got a counsellors' meeting."

* * *

"Sorry I'm late, guys," said Chip as he wearily entered the mess hall where the rest of the counsellors were assembled for the meeting. "I've got a real doozer of a cabin this month!"

"Me too!" exclaimed Ralph Deacon of Cabin 3. "They never go to sleep. They just talk all night."

"You're lucky," sighed Chip. "All mine want to do is fight. I've got this kid Miller—he won't do *anything*! All he does is stuff garbage in other kids' things. I don't know how you stood him, Pierre. He and his buddy spent all day in arts and crafts."

"No they didn't," said Pierre. "Arts and crafts was closed today."

Chip turned purple. "See what I mean? Now I'll never know where he was! He and Webster came back covered in mud and told me it was messy in arts and crafts! This is what I have to put up with! I'm only one person!"

"Calm down," soothed Dave, the swimming coach. "The poor kid's probably just homesick. That's what it sounds like to me."

"I thought so too at first," moaned Chip, "but now I'm beginning to wonder. You should have seen the letter he tried to write home. And all he ever says is 'I don't . . . I don't swim, I don't run, I don't anything.'

He's driving me crazy!"

"Aw, give him a chance," said Jack Tyler of Cabin 9. "A few more days and he'll be having fun like everybody else."

"But where were they? Where were they when they were supposed to be at arts and crafts? *Where*?"

4
Good, clean, wholesome fun

Mike Webster was dreaming. He was in jail, an inno-
cent man, and until he had met his cellmate, there had
been no hope. But now they were tunnelling and freedom was only a few metres away. He could feel his
cellmate tugging at him, urging him forward.

"I'm coming, I'm coming," mumbled Mike.

"Shh." Rudy's white face loomed over him in the
darkened cabin. "They're all asleep. Let's go."

Mike let himself down from the upper bunk and
silently struggled into his clothes. "What time is it?" he
whispered.

"A little after five," Rudy whispered back. "It'll be
daylight by the time we reach the mainland. Hurry
up."

The two boys tiptoed across the room and let themselves out of Cabin 13, taking great care to shut the
door noiselessly behind them. They raced through the
darkness to the waterfront and the dock.

"Look," said Mike nervously as Rudy selected a
small motorboat, "are you sure about this? I heard
someone say you can't swim."

"Of course I can swim," said Rudy, his poker face

expressing nothing. He paused. "What about you? Can you swim?"

"Sure. I wouldn't set foot in a boat if I couldn't. Anyway, here's two life jackets."

Rudy and Mike quickly donned the jackets and hopped into the boat. Rudy cast off from the dock and gave a mighty heave on the starter cord. The small outboard motor turned over and roared into life. Rudy cast Mike a look of triumph as the small boat pulled away from the dock and headed towards open water.

"How long do you think it'll take to get to the mainland?" shouted Mike over the engine noise. He cast a nervous eye back towards the sleeping island.

"Maybe ten or fifteen minutes," Rudy called back. "It's clear sailing from here on in."

The sky was just beginning to show the first streaks of dawn and the little outboard was about halfway to the mainland when Rudy and Mike first spotted the big Ontario Provincial Police cruiser. It shone a spotlight on them and then pulled alongside the small craft. An officer appeared and gazed down at the two boys.

"Hi," he said by way of greeting. "Where are you fellows going at this hour of the morning?"

"The mainland, sir," said Rudy.

"Are you from Algonkian?" asked the officer.

"Yes, sir," chorused the two boys.

"Well, now, let's check out your gear. Life jackets on correctly? ... Yup. Extra gas can? ... Yup. Emergency oars? ... Yup. Bailing bucket? ... What? No bailing bucket? Where's your bailing bucket?"

There was a long silence. "Darn it," Rudy said mildly, "we must have forgotten."

"No bailing bucket?" repeated the officer. "You just turn that rig around and go right back to camp. And don't come out again without a bailing bucket."

Obediently Rudy turned the boat around and headed back towards Algonkian Island.

"We got away with everything," said Mike bitterly, "and we forgot the bailing bucket!"

"No bailing bucket," repeated Rudy, half to himself.

With the patrol boat still in the area, Rudy piloted the outboard back to the Algonkian dock and moored it there.

"Come on," he said to Mike. "Back to our cell."

"That was *awful,*" breathed Mike.

"Oh well," Rudy shrugged, the image of Alcatraz Island strong in his mind. "At least we weren't fired on. And tomorrow's another day."

The two boys crossed the compound to Cabin 13 and let themselves in. Everyone was still asleep.

Rudy reached into his duffle bag, pulled out his chalk and drew another line on the cabin wall. "Three," he counted.

* * *

"Well, Miller," said Chip over breakfast that morning, "are you and Webster going to join our volleyball game today?"

"Gee, no," said Rudy blandly. "We're really more interested in arts and crafts."

"Yes, I thought so," said Chip cunningly. "Today before lunch I want to see that there *saleté* you're working on."

Mike turned deathly white.

"Certainly," said Rudy. "It should be ready by then.

Right, Mike?"

"If we hurry," agreed Mike in a strangled voice.

"Great," said Chip. "I'm really looking forward to seeing what keeps you glued to arts and crafts."

"As long as it keeps Miller away from us, it's fine!" said Harold Greene viciously.

Rudy stared at him pityingly.

"All right, you guys," bellowed Chip. "Out to the volleyball court. Miller, Webster, I'll see you *and* your *saleté* here at lunch."

He jogged off at the head of his troop.

"Now what are we going to do?" asked Mike miserably as he and Rudy walked into the empty cabin. "Chip wants to see our *saleté*. We haven't got a *saleté*. There's no such thing as a *saleté!*"

"Yes, there is," said Rudy. "I told you it means dirt."

"Well, how are we going to produce a *saleté* by lunchtime?"

"Shouldn't be too difficult," said Rudy. "There's plenty of dirt around." A sweep of his arm indicated his general surroundings.

"Yeah," agreed Mike. "But Chip expects some sort of art thing."

"What our resident clone expects is not important," said Rudy. "*Saleté* means dirt, and that's what he's getting."

"A bag of dirt?" asked Mike incredulously.

"Certainly not," said Rudy indignantly. "That would be cheap. We'll give him the dirt in a properly-made wooden box."

"Do they have wood at arts and crafts?" asked Mike.

"Probably," replied Rudy. "But it doesn't matter. We're not using that wood anyway." He rubbed his hands together with glee and almost smiled. "We're going to use the wooden slats that support Harold Greene's mattress."

Mike gasped. "You wouldn't!"

"Yes I would," said Rudy.

* * *

"His Cloneship will love this," mumbled Rudy, his mouth full of nails.

Mike secured the last hinge on the lid of the box. "Should we paint it?"

"It would look nicer," said Rudy, taking the nails from his mouth and putting them down on the table. "I see it sky-blue—symbolic, you know? The sky on the outside and the earth on the inside."

"I'll get the paint," laughed Mike.

"Tomorrow," Rudy said thoughtfully as they carefully daubed pale blue paint onto their creation, "we'll go earlier, and we'll take a sailboat to make sure we're not heard by any patrols."

"And a bailing bucket," added Mike. "Don't forget the bailing bucket."

"It was uppermost in my mind," said Rudy.

"How long will it take for this paint to dry?" asked Mike, leaning back to admire their handiwork.

"The jar said half an hour," Rudy replied. "Let's put it out in the sun to speed it up. It's almost lunch time, and we still have to fill it."

"How long will that take? There's dirt all over the compound."

"For a superior *saleté* one must use superior dirt,"

explained Rudy.

"I wonder what he'll say when we give it to him."

"Oh, that's easy. He'll say '*Miller!*' Or he just may say nothing at all. Overcome, you see?" Rudy glanced at his watch. "We'll soon find out."

Pierre, the arts and crafts counsellor, strolled over to inspect their work.

"That's a nice, neat job," he observed. "Well sanded."

"Thanks," said Mike.

"We used only the best wood," put in Rudy. "Aged and stress-tested."

"Stress-tested?" Pierre repeated. "For a little box like that? What are you planning to put in it?"

"Dirt," said Rudy. "It's a present for our counsellor."

Pierre stared at him. "Tell me," he said finally, "by any chance would your name be Miller?"

"Why, yes," said Rudy, coming perilously close to smiling. Chip had obviously been dropping his name at the counsellors' meetings. This pleased him immensely.

"Come on," urged Mike. "It's as dry as it's going to get. Let's—uh—finish it up and go for lunch."

"It was great meeting you," said Pierre dubiously. "I'm glad you enjoy arts and crafts."

"'Bye," said Mike.

The two boys left the arts and crafts cabin in search of superior dirt.

* * *

Chip rubbed his hands together with great glee.

"Miller and Webster are late for lunch," he gloated, looking around the mess hall. "I've got them now. They're going to have to admit they weren't in arts and crafts yesterday and they didn't build a *saleté*." He smiled. He was going to put them on work detail for the rest of their miserable lives.

"Well," said Harold sarcastically, "where are our two artists?"

"Shut up, Greene," said Chip absently. "They'll be here."

"Hey, look, Chip," called Adam from the end of the table. "Here they come."

Into the mess hall came Rudy and Mike, proudly bearing their *saleté* on a pillow. They threaded their way through the other tables, walked up to table 13, and held out the small blue box for Chip's inspection.

"Here it is," said Rudy, "The *saleté*."

Chip was dumbfounded. They had actually done it. They had actually built a *saleté*. He lifted the lid and looked inside. Dirt. It looked like dirt. Some topsoil, some clay, a few stones and the odd blade of grass. Dirt. He ran his fingers through it. Dirt. This couldn't be a *saleté*. He had looked it up this morning in the dictionary and had been unable to find it, but whatever it was, this couldn't be it.

He looked up at Mike. The boy's face was bright red. His eyes turned towards Rudy, whose expression was inscrutable, as usual. "Miller—" he began softly, threateningly.

Rudy's eyes displayed deep pain. "Don't you like it?"

"It's—it's—very interesting," stammered Chip.

"I think it stinks," piped up Harold Greene.

"That's because you have no soul," explained Rudy pleasantly.

"I'll bet that's my pillow too," accused Harold.

"Ah, you recognized it," said Rudy. "Very good."

"All right, you guys," shouted Chip. "Grab some lunch. This afternoon we're *all* playing field hockey." He smiled maliciously at Rudy. "Since you've already finished the *saleté,* you and Webster will play too."

"I don't play field hockey," said Rudy.

"Why not?" demanded Chip.

"I'm a pacifist," said Rudy. "Hockey is far too violent for me. Besides, Mike and I decided we'd spend the afternoon playing chess."

"Chess?" howled Chip. "*Chess?* At camp? With all the marvellous things to do around here, you two want to play *chess?* What do you say, Webster?"

"Chess is—fun," said Mike lamely.

"It sure is," said Rudy enthusiastically. "And having fun is what camp is all about. You said so yourself, Chip."

"Oh, let them play chess!" exclaimed Harold impatiently. "At least we'll be rid of them."

"Shut up, Greene!" snapped Chip. After three days that answer was becoming a conditioned reflex. He turned to Rudy and Mike. "All right. Just for today. But tomorrow you're joining the baseball team like everybody else."

Rudy looked significantly towards Mike. If all went well, there wouldn't be a tomorrow.

* * *

"I think he took it rather well," said Rudy, castling his

king into safety. "After all, it's not every day a clone is presented with a box of high-grade dirt."

Mike pushed his king's rook pawn. "He's not such a bad guy, you know."

"Agreed," said Rudy. "He just happens to be in the wrong place—in my way. I'm afraid he'll have to take his lumps as I dish them out."

The two exchanged queens. "Maybe," suggested Mike timidly, "we could just get kicked out instead of running away. You know, be real bad and stuff. If enough counsellors complain, the Warden will pack us off home."

"Ha!" said Rudy scornfully. "They'd never toss us out of here. To them we're money in the bank. Haven't you noticed with our clone? No matter what I do he comes up smiling. We could no more get kicked out of here than you could win this game."

"I'm not losing." Mike moved his knight defensively.

"Yes you are." Rudy slashed in with a bishop. "Checkmate."

* * *

"All right, you guys," bawled Chip, "I'm going to a counsellors' meeting. You get yourselves to bed, on the double!" He walked out of the cabin, the *saleté* tucked neatly under his arm.

Obediently the boys began to change into their pajamas for the night. Aside from a few flying articles of clothing, all was quite peaceful.

"What's going to happen?" whispered Mike.

"We'll soon find out," said Rudy. "Look. There he goes."

Harold Greene placed his hands on the bedpost and vaulted to his upper bunk.

Crash! The unsupported mattress gave way and dropped straight down onto an unsuspecting Adam Willis who had been making himself comfortable below.

"*Augh!*" screamed Harold who had tumbled down with it.

Muffled shouting came from under him. The other boys began rushing to the rescue.

Rudy ripped the sheets off the nearest bed and hurled them into the midst of the confusion. Mike, instantly grasping the spirit of the thing, began racing around the cabin tossing pillows at random into the milling group. Boys began throwing them back.

"*Rumble!*" shouted a deafening voice.

Mike stared in open-mouthed amazement. The shout had come from Rudy Miller—Rudy, who never raised his voice and never involved himself in anything. That same Rudy grabbed him, and the two of them shot out the door.

"Where are we going?"

"This brawl isn't big enough," Rudy explained calmly. "We're going for reinforcements." His eyes gleamed, although his face did not change expression. "And when it's all over, we can blame it on Harold Greene."

Mike doubled over, remembering. "Did you see him fall? I thought I was going to choke!"

Rudy walked up to Cabin 12, opened the door and leaned inside. "Pardon me," he said politely. "There's a pillow fight in Cabin 13. If you'd like to take part, you're quite welcome." Leaving the door open, he stepped aside, pulling Mike with him. A stream of pajama-clad boys roared out the door, waving pillows and stampeding towards Cabin 13.

"Enthusiastic, aren't they?" commented Rudy.

The door of Cabin 11 burst open and a voice called, "What's going on?"

"Big pillow fight in 13!" hollered one of the boys from Cabin 12. "Come on! It's going to be a lulu!"

Rudy and Mike stepped out of the way just in time to avoid the onrush from Cabin 11.

"Rudy," said Mike nervously, "what are we going to do?"

"Do?" said Rudy. "We're going to sit down right here on the grass and watch."

Cabin 13 appeared to bulge at the seams, to bounce and gyrate. Feathers from torn pillows fluttered through the open door and windows. Joyous shouts of combat came from within. The only discordant note to what seemed a grand party was the half-crazed voice of Adam Willis, which pierced the night air: "All right, Greene! Now you're gonna *die*!"

Mike noticed a gleam in Rudy's eye.

Even as they watched, the doors of Cabin 14 burst open and another dozen boys rushed to join the fray, brandishing pillows. They were lost in the swirling clouds of feathers.

"Wow, look at that!" exclaimed Mike, half in horror.

Rudy nodded. "Camp," he said with an elaborate sweep of his arm. "Good, clean, wholesome fun. I wonder if they keep extra pillows in stock?"

* * *

"I tell you, it's a box of dirt. Nothing but a box of dirt!" exclaimed Chip angrily.

Pierre gaped in amazement at the box he had seen Rudy and Mike build. "I thought they were just being snarky when they told me they were going to fill it with dirt," he said, shaking his head. "They sure are strange kids, especially that guy Miller."

"Strange isn't the word I'd use for Miller," growled Chip. "Crazy would be more like it." He banged his fist on the table. "I don't like being lied to! They said they were building a *saleté*, and *this* is what they hand me!"

Pierre laughed out loud. "And that's exactly what you got—a *saleté*." He stopped to catch his breath. "It's French, Chip. It means dirt!"

Chip was struck dumb. For a moment he stared at the blue box as if hoping that the fury in his eyes would vaporize it. Then, "Of course I know that *saleté* means dirt!" he howled furiously. "Do you think I'm stupid?" He stood up, his face bright red. "Excuse me," he said. "I've got to do something back at the cabin." He went out the door of the mess hall on the dead run.

"Miller!" he muttered as he headed towards Cabin 13. "Miller!"

A steadily increasing roar met his ears as he ran. The general noise separated itself into individual shouting voices and falling furniture. He put on a burst of speed, rounded the sports equipment shed and stopped short.

Cabin 13 was teeming, both inside and out, with pajama-clad boys merrily swinging at each other with pillows amid a snowstorm of feathers. The ruckus had grown, and by now most of the camp was involved.

Chip's anguished eyes caught sight of two figures sitting passively on the grass. He charged up, howling, "*Miller!* What's going on here?"

"I think it's a pillow fight," offered Rudy.

"What are you doing out here?"

"I don't fight," said Rudy evenly.

"What started this?" cried Chip frantically.

"It was all Harold Greene's fault," tattled Rudy. "He jumped on Adam for no reason at all."

Arms flailing wildly, Chip rushed towards his cabin. He could not get near the door. "Break it up! *Break it—!*" He was hit full in the face with a pillow which exploded and sent more feathers flying everywhere. Chip came up sneezing and blowing short blasts on his whistle. Now on his hands and knees, he made another attempt to get inside Cabin 13, sneezing and howling madly.

Rudy pointed towards the mess hall. "Look. A thundering herd of clones," he observed. "Now the feathers will really fly."

Mike, who had not stopped laughing since Harold Greene's fall, could not reply.

The ground trembled and whistles shrilled as the counsellors hurled themselves into the heart of the ruckus. For the next few minutes the area boiled like a volcano. Pillows shot around like lightning bolts, and the feathers were so thick they obstructed all vision. Then, slowly, the riot began to peter out. Still, it was a full ten minutes before the air cleared and silence fell.

Slowly, and with much effort, Chip got to his feet. His face flaming red, he walked through the crowd, which parted in front of him, sensing the intensity of his emotions. Still he walked, until he was directly facing the side wall of the cabin. He stared at it for what seemed like a long time. Then he threw his head back, roared his anger to the sky, lifted his foot and dealt the cabin a mighty kick.

Crack!

A large chunk of the cabin wall splintered away and fell inside the building. A long, jagged split appeared in the wall itself, extending from the hole all the way up to the window. The widow frame came loose and the glass shattered. The split divided into a number of smaller cracks which spidered through the wood up to the roof. A lone roof shingle jarred loose and fell to the ground, landing at Chip's feet with a soft thud. He looked down at it incredulously as the breeze whistled softly through the gaping hole in the cabin.

There was an awful silence.

"Say," came the dry voice of Rudy Miller, "it looks as if we're going to have to sleep in trees after all."

* * *

Deep in the wooded area beside the creek, the beaver stirred restlessly. Once again human noise had disturbed him. There had been loud noises when his old dam was destroyed. This dam must remain safe.

5
Land ho!

It was three o'clock when Rudy and Mike tiptoed out of the emergency tent which had been hastily erected for the former occupants of the now uninhabitable Cabin 13.

"Two hours sleep!" moaned Mike as they made their way to the dock. The boys had been up until one digging in the rubble for their belongings and setting up the emergency tent to shelter themselves for the night. "Why can't we escape when we've had some rest?"

"There'll never be a better time than this," Rudy insisted. "The clones are all so exhausted that they wouldn't wake up if we fired a cannon in the compound." His eyes scanned the boats bobbing at the dock. "Here's a nice little sailboat. And there's a fairly good breeze." He nodded, satisfied. "We should be on the mainland in no time."

"It's too dark," mumbled Mike, struggling into his life jacket.

"It's only dark," said Rudy, "because you haven't opened your eyes yet. Snap out of it. It's going to take two of us to get this thing across the water." He buckled himself into his own life jacket.

"I'm tired."

"Life jackets on correctly?" snapped Rudy crisply. "Yup. Emergency oars? . . . Yup. Bailing bucket? . . . Hey, we've even got a bailing bucket. How about that?"

"Extra gas can. You forgot extra gas can."

"No, thank you, sir," said Rudy. "This is a sailboat. And may I remind you that there will be no sleeping on board by passengers or crew. We will be leaving port in five seconds. Since you still have one foot on the dock, I recommend that you make up your mind."

Mike jumped aboard and looked oddly at his companion. It was remarkable how even the thought of leaving Algonkian Island managed to animate Rudy's personality.

Rudy ran up the sail and slowly the boat began to creep away from the dock.

"Ahoy, there, Webster. Look alive or I'll have you swabbing the deck."

"Do you have to do that?" grumbled Mike.

"Yes, I have to do that," explained Rudy. "You're falling asleep. Take a new port-starboard heading! Man the poop deck! Trim the mains'l! Avast, ye swab!"

"I can't go port and starboard at the same time," growled Mike. "We have no poop deck. And that's not just the mainsail—it's our only sail!"

"You do refuse to enter into the spirit of the thing, don't you?" said Rudy with mock dejection. "We're moving along really well, I think." He shaded his eyes in his best seafaring manner. "Thar she blows!"

"There what blows?" asked Mike, annoyed. He sat

up suddenly, eyes wide, and pointed to the limp sail. "Nothing blows! Nothing! Rudy, we've lost the wind. What are we going to do? We're only a third of the way across."

"It doesn't matter," said Rudy confidently. "We've got a long time until reveille. After last night the clones won't want the prisoners up until eight or nine. The current will take us the rest of the way by then."

"I don't know," said Mike anxiously. "Maybe we should start rowing."

"Go right ahead," invited Rudy. "I'm going to sit back, relax and let the current do the work."

"Well, I guess you're right," Mike conceded. "For a little while anyway, until we see how things go."

The two boys reclined in the becalmed sailboat. Tiny waves lapped against the hull and the small craft drifted aimlessly. Soon Rudy and Mike were fast asleep.

* * *

A sudden jar and an odd scraping sound brought Mike Webster to awareness. "Hey, we're here! We're here! Rudy, wake up! We made it!"

Rudy snapped to attention. It was still dark—a little past five according to the luminous face on his watch. The boat had beached itself on a sand bar not five metres from shore. "Land ho," he commented blandly. "Now, wasn't that better than rowing?"

Mike nodded enthusiastically.

"Okay," said Rudy briskly, "time to set the boat adrift. Where's the note?"

"I thought you were bringing the note."

Rudy sighed. "Must I do everything? Oh well, we'll

just set it adrift without a note. They'll figure it out."

The two scrambled out of the sailboat, pushed it out towards the open water and waded ashore.

"Where to?" asked Mike.

"Just walk," said Rudy, "directly away from the lake." He reached into his pocket and produced a shiny dime. "You see this dime? When we reach a pay phone, this is our ticket home. I've been saving it since the day I arrived at Alcatraz."

They trudged in silence for a while.

"You know," said Mike suddenly, "I don't think my folks are going to be too pleased with the fact that I ran away from camp."

"Oh, mine won't either," said Rudy, "and Guidance will be most distressed. But after a while they'll get used to the idea. They always do." His eyes gleamed in the darkness. "The one thing I regret about leaving camp is that I won't get to witness Harold Greene's punishment for starting the riot."

"Yeah," agreed Mike, grinning. "Chip is so mad he's likely to put him on work detail for years. Serves him right too, the twit!"

Rudy wrinkled his nose. "We're getting close to civilization. I smell garbage." He tossed his dime up in the air and caught it deftly. "Where there's garbage, there's people, and where there's people, there's a telephone." He was almost smiling.

"Sun's coming up," commented Mike.

Rudy consulted his watch. "Ten to six," he announced. "Look, there's a clearing up ahead. Civilization. People. Telephones."

Both boys broke into a run. They came out of the trees into the clearing and stopped dead, mouths agape. There was the wash station. And the baseball diamond. And the mess hall. And Cabins 1 through 22, including the damaged 13.

"This," said Rudy quietly, "is obviously not civilization."

Mike stepped forward and spread his arms wide. "But how?"

"*You* were steering," Rudy pointed out.

"You fell asleep too!"

"Yes, but *I* wasn't steering."

Mike sat down on the grass. "I don't want to be back here," he said simply. "I want to go home. Let's get another boat."

"Too late," said Rudy, eyeing the sunrise. "The clones would catch us right in the middle of the lake. But tomorrow's another day." He grimaced. "It's a good thing we didn't put a note in that boat explaining how we'd run off. We'd look awfully stupid. And we'd also haul garbage even longer than Harold Greene."

Mike hung his head and scratched at the turf. "I'm sorry," he said. "It's all my fault. If I hadn't fallen asleep we'd be on our way home by now."

Rudy shrugged. "I accept your apology."

Mike stared at him. "You mean you're not going to shoulder one bit of the blame?"

"Why should I?" asked Rudy. "I wasn't steering."

Mike laughed in spite of himself. Rudy was, after all, Rudy, and that was that.

Walking over to Cabin 13 Rudy wriggled gingerly through the hole in the side wall and stepped gracefully through the ankle-deep feathers to what had been his corner. From his pocket he produced the chalk and drew a fourth line beside the other three on the wall.

"Four," he counted wearily.

* * *

"Well, you guys," said Chip at the breakfast table, "there'll be no activities for you today."

"Drat the luck," said Rudy, poker-faced. "I was planning on a little baseball, soccer, swimming, volleyball, badminton, obstacle course, field hockey and darts. And then, *after* lunch—"

"Miller, cut that out!" bellowed Chip. "We've got a cabin to fix up! If you guys are going to act like animals you're going to have to miss some of the fun!"

"May I remind you," said Rudy quietly, "that it was not one of us who kicked in the wall."

"Shut up!" mumbled Chip.

"Yeah, shut up!" snarled Harold Greene. "I bet it was your fault last night!"

"You'd have a hard time proving that," said Rudy, "considering you're the one who jumped on Adam."

"The bed was broken!"

"Of course it was broken. You kept on hurling yourself onto it. What did you expect?"

"You are nothing but a nut!" screamed Harold.

"And you're a twit!" shouted Mike.

"Now let's not lose our tempers," said Rudy quietly.

"You guys are both crazy! We haven't got one nut! We've got two!"

"Two nuts and a twit!" Mike counted, red-faced.

"And no cabin," Rudy added.

"Cool it, you guys!" yelled Chip.

"Stay out of this!" chorused Mike and Harold furiously.

Angrily Chip doubled his fist and hit the table with

a mighty crash. A leg snapped, the table tilted, and an assortment of trays and dishes slid off onto the floor.

There was a shocked silence, broken by Rudy's dry voice: "I can just see the headline: *Table Destroyed At Alcatraz, toll of phantom wood-butcher rises to two.*"

A piercing hoot escaped Mike Webster. He broke into gales of laughter.

Chip pointed in turn to Harold, Mike and Rudy. "Work detail! Work detail! *Work detail!*"

They were interrupted by the appearance of Frank, the head counsellor, in the doorway. "Attention, everybody. All campers and staff are to report to the baseball diamond after breakfast. Mr. Warden has something to say to us."

"And I've got something to say to him," commented Rudy. "His legs are crooked."

Mike's laughter swelled again.

Chip pointed at him and then at Rudy. "Work detail! Work detail!"

"Yes, yes," soothed Rudy.

* * *

"Now, let's see," said Rudy as he and Mike settled themselves among the crowd on the baseball diamond. "I got two days work detail and you got two days work detail, but little Harold got only one. It looks as if twits have a higher standing than nuts around here."

Mike was just getting himself back under control. "Oh, Rudy, don't make me laugh! *Please* don't make me laugh when the Warden comes!"

All eyes were drawn to the camp director's cottage at the edge of the baseball field. The front door opened and Mr. Warden emerged, smartly dressed in a white tennis outfit. He strutted briskly to the small platform that Frank had set up for him, mounted it and reached for the microphone.

"Look," murmured Rudy, "you can see half the camp through his legs."

Mike held his head. Surviving this assembly without receiving more work detail wasn't going to be easy.

"Good morning, boys," said Mr. Warden sternly. It was obvious to all that the director was furious. "You all know why I've called you here this morning. I'm referring to the outrageous events of last night. I have no doubt that most of you were involved."

"Some more than others," said Rudy, staring at Harold Greene.

"Rudy – " whispered Mike warningly. Chip was glaring in their direction.

"Now, boys," said the director, "this is Camp Algonkian Island. It was founded thirty-one years ago by my grandfather, Elias Warden, and in all that time, not once before last night has any wanton destruction occurred. Much damage was caused by your foolish- · ness, damage that must be repaired at the camp's expense. Since you have proved that you cannot be trusted on your own, in future, patrols will be posted during counsellors' meetings. Meanwhile, you will all take turns assisting the boys of Cabin 13 in repairing their unit. That takes priority over everything."

He paused to let his words sink in. "It would benefit campers, *and* counsellors," he added, glaring at Chip, "if we all learned to practise a little self-control.

"And one more thing—a two-man sailboat is missing from the dock. There can be only two reasons for this, both of them unacceptable to me. Either the boat was improperly tied and drifted away, or someone has taken it without permission. Whoever is responsible had better own up soon.

"Your counsellors will tell you what hours you will be working on Cabin 13. See that the events of last night are not repeated. Good day."

"Gee, he's crabby," remarked Rudy.

* * *

Groups of campers spent the morning clearing out the wreckage of Cabin 13, salvaging bedding and whatever reusable lumber they could find. Shortly before noon two professional carpenters arrived by launch from the mainland.

"*Miller!*" Chip shouted at one point, "You get in there and help!"

"I don't salvage," was Rudy's reply.

"The heck you don't!"

So Rudy bent his back the same as everyone else.

"Sentenced to one month hard labour," Rudy recited, hauling a mattress out to air on the grass, "the Noble Nuts are forced to toil endlessly in the hot sun for the satisfaction of the dreaded clone taskmasters."

"This is definitely slave labour!" grunted Mike, beating the dust out of a pillow.

"Come on, you guys!" shouted Chip. "Hurry it up! Keep moving!" He walked up to Rudy. "Do you know anything about that missing sailboat, Miller?"

"I don't sail," said Rudy.

"I'm not surprised to hear that," said Chip. "All right, you guys," he bellowed, "break for lunch! Wash station first!"

"I don't know about you," said Rudy as he and

Mike entered the wash station, "but they've seen the last of me on that job site. My parents sent me to camp to have fun."

Mike splashed water onto his sweaty face. "How are you going to get out of it?"

"I'm going to get poisoned from lunch and sleep it off in the infirmary," Rudy decided. "With my radio. Miraculously, it survived the disaster."

"They found my guitar," said Mike forlornly. "Smashed."

"Alcatraz will probably pay for the repairs," said Rudy. "After all, it got smashed in *their* cabin which was destroyed by *their* campers. And the finishing touch was delivered by *their* clone. Hey," he went on, "I wonder if anyone's fixed our mess table. We may have to eat off the floor."

"That'll be okay for you," said Mike. "It'll be easier to get poisoned off the floor. I'm going to have to work this afternoon."

"Why don't you get poisoned too?" suggested Rudy. "I'm sure there's plenty of poison to go around."

Mike shook his head. "I'd better not. They'd get suspicious if there were two of us. You go ahead."

The boys arrived in the mess hall to find that table 13 had been replaced by a long sheet of plywood resting on two sawhorses. Because the sawhorses were of slightly different sizes, the new table had a pronounced slope.

Mike put down his tray and watched helplessly as his orange rolled away towards the end of the table. It hit the edge of Chip's tray, bounced into the air and landed with a resounding *plop!* in the counsellor's soup.

"Nice shot," commented Rudy dryly. "You gave him a real snootful."

"Cut the comedy," snapped Chip, wiping the soup off his face. "All right, you guys, hurry up. We've got a job to do this afternoon."

"And don't eat anything round," advised Rudy. He tasted his tomato soup. "Hey, this tastes spoiled!"

"It's not spoiled," said Chip.

"Well, you ought to know. You're covered in it." Rudy finished his soup, making sour faces all the while. Then he turned to his hot dog and took a bite. "Ugh! Where do they store the meat? Out in the sun?"

"There's nothing wrong with those hot dogs, Miller," said Chip warningly. "Eat."

Rudy ate, and when the last bite was gone he doubled over on the bench and gasped, "You made me eat and now I'm sick!"

"He's not sick," sneered Harold Greene. "He's just trying to get out of working this afternoon."

"Shut up, Greene!" snapped Chip. He turned to Rudy. "You're not sick, Miller! You're just trying to get out of working this afternoon!"

"I'm sick," said Rudy. "And if I don't get to the infirmary soon I'm going to die at your hands, just like the cabin and the table."

"That does it!" growled Chip. "There was nothing wrong with the food and there's nothing wrong with you. Now sit up straight and save your strength. You're going to need it for this afternoon."

"If I die . . . " warned Rudy.

"I'll take that chance!"

* * *

"We're lucky," commented Rudy, heaving a huge garbage bag into his wheelbarrow. "We got off work so we could serve our work detail. Isn't camp fun?"

"Ugh! Spaghetti!" exclaimed Mike, taping a torn bag. He laughed. "Did you notice that Chip sat at the high end of the table at supper? Good thing too."

"Yeah," agreed Rudy. "After all, it was His Cloneship who spilled the spaghetti that came oozing down at Harold Greene. That twit'll be picking spaghetti out of his lap for the duration."

Mike laughed again. "Anyway, we'll have a roof over our heads tonight. The wall's back up and they're setting up the bunks now." He grasped the handles of the wheelbarrow and started down the path. "Are we going to give escaping another shot tomorrow?"

Rudy shook his head. "I'd like to, but it's not practical," he replied. "The clones are really watching the dock since that sailboat—ahem—disappeared. Let's give it another day and see what happens."

They approached the dump to find Harold Greene already there emptying his wheelbarrow.

"Well," said Rudy. "Observe the typical Algonkian Twit in its natural habitat."

"Shut up, Miller! It's your fault I got work detail! Everything is your fault!"

"I try," said Rudy modestly.

"Oh, you make me so *mad*!" screamed Harold.

"That's because you're so *nasty*!" shouted Mike.

"You two leave me alone," warned Harold, "or I'll tell Chip you attacked me."

"Liar!" shouted Mike, outraged. "Twit!"

"Kindly move out of the way," said Rudy to Harold. "I'm dumping my garbage."

"Webster, you're even worse than *him*! You're a real nut!"

"How'd you like to eat this garbage?" warned Mike.

"*Nut*!" screamed Harold in a white-hot rage. "*Nut*!"

"*Twit*!" Mike screamed back. "Bonehead! Skunk!"

"*Awwww*!" Blindly Harold stormed out of the clearing in the wrong direction.

Rudy cupped his hand to his ear with something almost like a smile on his face.

Splash!

"He's in the creek!" crowed Mike. "Harold fell in the creek!"

"Help!" came a gurgling voice.

"Come on," said Rudy wearily. "Let's go fish him out."

"I suppose we have to," said Mike sadly.

Rudy nodded.

Each hauling on an arm, Rudy and Mike pulled Harold to his feet in the shallow water of the creek.

"I'll fix you!" he spluttered. "I'm going to tell Chip you threw me in!"

"Well, in that case . . ." said Rudy. His eyes met Mike's. Both boys nodded. They dropped Harold back into the water.

*   *   *

"And Greene says they threw him in the creek, and Miller says he fell in," finished Chip at the counsellors' meeting later that night.

"Well," said Dave, "it's obvious Miller's lying."

"That's what I said to him" said Chip. "And do you know what his answer was? 'I don't lie.' And do you know what? I believe him. He may be everything else in the world, but a liar he isn't."

"Chip," began Frank, the head counsellor, "we've been doing quite a bit of talking about your kid Miller, and we've decided that he's a real problem."

"Well, hallelujah," said Chip, chin in hand. "Now tell me something I don't know." He looked up suddenly, eyes anxious. "That sounded like Miller! I'm starting to sound like Miller!"

"Just take it easy," soothed Frank. "Don't let the kid get to you. Tomorrow all your problems will be solved."

"How?" asked Chip. "Are you going to drown Miller? Would you do Greene too? And maybe Webster?"

"Tomorrow," said Frank determinedly, "we're all going to make your Miller take part in our sports program—and we've got an extensive one planned."

Chip was not impressed. "*You* tell him," he said.

"Don't worry," promised Frank. "We'll tell him."

* * *

The beaver was still trembling. The sound and smell of humans was often in the woods, but this had been different. One of them had been in the water, dangerously close to the unfinished dam. Nothing must interfere with his work. Nothing must harm the dam.

6
Did you see that?

"Well, Miller," said Chip cheerfully at breakfast the next morning, "it's a beautiful day."

"If you mean that the table is back, then yes, it *is* a beautiful day," said Rudy. "Otherwise, I disagree heartily." He put his tray down beside where Mike was sitting and began to eat his breakfast.

"Oh, I wouldn't disagree so soon," said Chip, enjoying himself immensely. "We have some great activities planned for today."

"Oh, too bad," said Rudy sadly. "I'm going to be busy all day."

Chip laughed delightedly. "Yes, I know. In fact, this is going to be the busiest day you've ever had."

Rudy cocked his head and glanced at his counsellor curiously. Something was in the wind.

"I don't like the sound of that," whispered Mike. "He's up to something."

Rudy shrugged indifferently and continued eating.

Just as he finished his breakfast, Frank and three of the other counsellors approached table 13 and stationed themselves behind him. "You're Miller," said the head counsellor.

"I knew that," replied Rudy lightly.

'Well, here's something you may not know," said Frank. "This morning you're playing baseball and soccer, and before lunch you're going swimming."

"I don't play baseball or soccer," said Rudy calmly, "and I don't swim. Lunch we can negotiate."

"Maybe you didn't hear me," returned Frank firmly. "I'm not asking you—I'm telling you. Now, as I was saying, that's the morning. We'll tell you about the afternoon later."

"You mean," said Rudy, staring straight ahead, "I don't get any choice?"

"Oh, you get a choice," said Frank. "You can play—or you can play."

Rudy nodded slowly. "That seems fair enough. I accept."

"That means you too, Webster," put in Chip. "How do you like them apples, Miller?"

Rudy just stared at him through half-closed eyes.

* * *

"All right, Miller," called Chip from behind the backstop. "You're up first."

Rudy glared at him, selected a bat and stepped up to the plate, assuming a right-handed stance.

"Hey, Chip, aren't you going to tell him which end to hold?" called Harold Greene from the players' bench.

"Shut up, Greene," said Chip absently. He could not take his eyes off Rudy, who was standing in the batter's box with his feet quite close together, his knees turned slightly inwards. "You'll get more power, Miller, if you spread those feet a little."

Rudy ignored him and remained like a statue in his odd stance. The pitcher wound up and threw a straight fastball, right into the strike zone. Rudy reared back his left leg and stepped into the pitch. The swing made a whining sound in the air.

Tock! The ball soared up and away and was out of sight instantly. Rudy rounded the bases, a bored expression on his face.

"That's the hardest hit ball I've ever seen!" cried Chip as Rudy crossed the plate. "It went way out there! Way out!"

"Wow!" said Ralph Deacon, the opposing coach. "Nobody can hit a ball that far!"

"Miller can!" howled Chip. "He just did! I saw it!" He turned to Frank, who was acting as scorekeeper. "One to nothing! Mark that down! All right, Greene, you're up next. Let's see you do that."

Harold struck out, swinging wildly at the first three pitches. Then Tony Delsey popped out and Brian Meadows grounded out to retire the side.

"All right, you guys," ordered Chip, "take the field. Miller, you play second base."

The batter wound up and lobbed a fat one right over the plate. *Crack!* Chip groaned. It was a line drive just over the pitcher's head, and sure to be good for at least two bases. From out of nowhere flew Rudy Miller. He leaped, stuck out his glove and picked the well-hit ball right out of the air.

"Did you see that?" screamed Chip. "That was the greatest catch in the history of baseball! I've never seen anything like it before in my whole life! What a play!"

In that inning, Rudy stopped a hot grounder and

threw to first base for the second out, and then caught an almost impossible short fly ball for the third out.

"What a catch!" Chip was raving. "I've never seen an infielder run backwards like that! One to nothing! It's still one to nothing! We're winning!"

As the next Cabin 13 batter stepped up to the plate, Rudy sat down on the bench beside Mike. Mike looked at him oddly. "Rudy, do you do stuff like that all the time?"

"Only when I'm playing baseball," said Rudy sourly, "which is usually never, if I can help it."

"Chip is having hysterics," said Mike.

"It doesn't take much," said Rudy. "I'm sure you've noticed that."

"Well, Andy struck out," said Mike. "I'm up. Got any pointers for me?"

"No," said Rudy coldly.

The next two innings went quickly. Rudy, switched to centre field, ended the third inning with the miraculous catch of a sure homerun ball, followed up by a long throw to first base to catch the runner trying to tag up.

"That was the most amazing double play in the whole world!" raved Chip. "What a throw! It didn't even bounce! What an arm! Wow! We're still ahead," he reminded Frank. "Still one to nothing. And Miller's up this inning!"

Adam, the Cabin 13 pitcher, struck out feebly, and that brought Rudy to the plate.

"Come on, Miller!" cheered Chip. "Do it again!"

"He could never do it again," piped up Harold Greene. "It was a fluke." He got a catcher's mitt right in the mouth from Mike Webster.

The first pitch was low and outside. Ball one, thought Chip. But Rudy crouched down, moved forward and reached for the ball.

Tock! Like its predecessor, this ball soared fast and far and out of sight. Expressionless, Rudy ran the bases.

Chip cheered himself hoarse. "That one must have flown all the way to the dump! Bring on another ball!" He turned to Frank. "That's two to nothing. We've got two runs now!"

Harold Greene walked, and it looked like the beginning of a rally for Cabin 13, but Tony Delsey hit into a double play to retire the side.

"All right, Miller, you're pitching!" ordered Chip joyfully.

Obediently Rudy took the mound. He burned nine consecutive strikes past baffled Cabin 3 batters. When he got to the bench, Mike Webster was blowing on his sore catching hand.

Chip was gibbering by this time. "What an arm! What an arm! Nine strikes! Wow! Two to nothing," he reminded Frank.

Frank walked over to Chip. "Say—uh—Chip, can I have a word with you?"

"Not now! Not now! Can't you see we're in the middle of a game? And it's two to nothing! For *us*!"

"Hey," said Frank, "haven't you been holding out on us a little about this kid Miller?"

"Holding out? I told you he wouldn't play!"

"Yeah, well he's played someplace. A guy who's that good—"

"We'll talk about it later," said Chip. "All right, you guys, up to bat. Let's get some hits here! Can't let

Miller do all the work, right, Miller?"

Rudy just glared at him.

It was the sixth inning and the score was still 2-0 when Rudy came up to bat again. The pitcher wound up and threw a low ball that broke to the inside and clipped Rudy on the back of the leg.

"What are you trying to do?" screamed Chip. Only the efforts of Adam and Mike prevented him from going for Ralph Deacon's throat. "You dusted him off just because you knew he was going to hit another home run! Miller, *Miller*, are you all right? Speak to me! Can you walk?"

With a contemptuous glance over his shoulder at his counsellor, Rudy jogged down to first base.

"All right, Greene," shouted Chip. "Bring him home. Let's get some hits out there!"

No sooner did the ball leave the pitcher's hand than Rudy was off like a shot. The infield was taken so much by surprise that he went into second base standing up.

"What speed!" bawled Chip. "I've never seen anybody move that fast! He didn't even have to slide! All right, Greene, you've got one strike! Now get a hit!"

Rudy took a long lead off second base, ignoring the signals from Chip, who had assumed the coaching spot behind third. Suddenly the pitcher wheeled and threw to the shortstop, who was covering second. Opting not to go back, Rudy took off for third. Kicking up a huge cloud of dust, he slid in just under the tag.

"You're just a blue streak!" Chip bellowed right in Rudy's ear. "Attaway, Miller!"

Rudy stood up, brushed himself off and scowled at his counsellor.

65

On the second pitch, Harold swung mightily and managed to hit a dribbling grounder that oozed out towards the mound.

Rudy took off like a gazelle, his feet hardly touching the ground.

"No, Miller! No! Stay put!" cried Chip.

The pitcher fumbled at the ball, then scooped it up and threw it home. But the catcher's eyes were on Rudy, bearing down on him like a freight train. The ball bounced off his mask, and as he stooped to retrieve it, Rudy dove between his feet and tagged home. Safe. Almost as an afterthought, the catcher picked up the ball and threw to first. Harold Greene was out.

"Did you see that?" Chip was delirious. "Did you actually *see* that? It was—it was—it's three to nothing! We've got three runs! He stole home! And we've got a man on—Oh no! Greene, what were you doing? Sightseeing or something? A turtle could have made it to first!"

By the end of the ninth inning, Cabin 13 was ahead four to nothing, Rudy having hit a third home run.

Chip was in ecstasy. "We *won!* We finally won a game! It was the most amazing incredible fantastic stupendous game in baseball history! Miller, you said you couldn't play baseball!"

"I never said I couldn't," said Rudy blandly. "I said I don't."

Frank walked up to Chip. "Congratulations," he said coldy. "I guess you've got the camp championship all sewed up."

"I guess so," chortled Chip gleefully. "Isn't Miller something?"

"At baseball," said Frank grimly. "Let's see if he

can play soccer." He turned to Rudy. "I suppose you don't play soccer."

"That's right," said Rudy hopefully. "I don't."

"Well, you're going to," said the head counsellor. "Cabin 13, get over to the soccer field. Cabin 9 is waiting for you."

As the boys made their way to the soccer field, Mike jogged up to Rudy. "I'm sorry."

"For what?" Rudy asked listlessly.

"For asking you for batting tips," said Mike.

"I accept your apology."

Mike laughed to himself. Some things changed, but Rudy never did.

"All right, you guys!" bellowed Chip. "Take the field and play your positions! Miller, you're a forward." He turned to Jack Tyler, the Cabin 9 counsellor. "Jack, we just won a baseball game that you wouldn't believe!"

"Oh, yes, I would!" exclaimed Jack. "I was walking across the compound when that home-run ball nearly took my head off. So I came to watch the rest of the game. The whole camp's buzzing about your Miller. You kept him a secret, didn't you?"

"No!" Chip's denial was vehement. "He kept himself a secret! He wouldn't play!"

"A star like that? Don't make me laugh!"

"But—" said Chip.

The game was under way. Instantly Rudy stole the ball and manoeuvred his way through the Cabin 9 defence in a manner which left many of them sprawled on the grass. Effortlessly he approached the opposing goal and kicked. Like a cannonball, the ball went into the top right-hand corner of the net. The goalie did not even see it, and made no move.

"Did you see that? He deked out the whole team! What feet! And what a kick! It's a wonder the ball isn't flat as a pancake!"

Chip turned to Frank, who was acting as scorekeeper, but before he could open his mouth the head counsellor said sourly. "Yes, I know. One to nothing for you. I've already marked it down. I guess you think you've been pretty cute about this kid Miller."

"Honest," cried Chip earnestly, "I'm the most surprised guy in the place! I thought he'd be a dud, not wanting to play and all. I just don't understand it." He glanced towards the field. "Hey, Miller's got the ball again! Come on, Miller! Pass!"

"Who's he going to pass to?" asked Frank bitterly. "Nobody on the field can keep up with him."

"A goal! A goal!" cheered Chip. "Two to nothing! Mark that down!"

When the game ended, Cabin 13 had won, 18-0. Rudy Miller had scored ten of those goals and assisted on six others.

* * *

"Oh," said Dave, the swimming coach, "you're the guy who can't swim."

After their second amazing victory, the boys of Cabin 13 were standing around on the swimming pier awaiting their turn in the water.

Frank elbowed Chip in the stomach. "There goes your living legend," he gloated. "Miller can't swim."

"Well, we'll take care of that," promised Dave. "Go get a flutterboard and I'll teach you how to kick."

"You'd better get him a rubber ducky," sneered Harold Greene.

68

"Shut up, Greene!" ordered Chip. "That'll cost you another day's work detail!"

"Okay, everybody," said Dave, "into the water. Recreational swimming while I work with Miller."

Passively Rudy allowed himself to be led into the water and draped over a styrofoam flutterboard. He had been kicking around in a small circle, earning Dave's praise, when he heard an angry shout from the pier.

"Greene," bawled Chip "you're beyond the limit! Get back in here!"

"I can't!" quavered Harold from way out. "I've got a cramp!"

Instantly Chip threw himself into the water and began splashing out towards Harold. "Wait here!" shouted Dave to Rudy, and he too began swimming towards Harold.

As Rudy watched, Harold went under for a few seconds and came up sputtering.

"That twit," Rudy commented aloud. He tossed aside his flutterboard and began to swim long, powerful strokes that carried him swiftly through the water. He passed Dave and began to pull ahead of Chip.

"*Miller*! Get back there! You can't swim!"

Rudy reached the struggling Harold well ahead of the two counsellors. Grasping him in approved Red Cross fashion, Rudy began a powerful side-stroke which soon brought the two of them back to the pier. He boosted Harold up to Frank's waiting arms, retrieved his drifting flutterboard and resumed his kicking.

Chip and Dave swam up. Dave snatched the board away from Rudy and turned to Chip. "He can't swim, eh?" He brought the flutterboard down on top of

Chip's head. It broke in two.

* * *

"You might have told me you could swim like that!" said Chip at the lunch table.

"You didn't ask," said Rudy.

"I'm not complaining," explained Chip hastily. "You were just great out there this morning." He surveyed the boys at table 13. "This is a great day. We're just starting to click as a team."

"A team?" laughed Adam ruefully. "Miller did it all by himself. He could have beaten those guys without us. In fact, I think we got in his way."

"No way!" insisted Chip. "We're a team. Right, guys?"

"Right," they all chorused, tiredly and without much conviction.

Rudy took a bite of his sandwich. "Hey, this tastes stale."

Chip flushed. "No, Miller, you're not poisoned. Heh, heh, great little kidder, that Miller."

Mike nudged Rudy. "You're not going to go berserk and kill somebody, are you?"

"I can't guarantee anything," replied Rudy evenly.

Mike grinned. "Tell me," he said, "what happens when you play other sports?"

Rudy shrugged. "Same thing."

Mike whistled. "I don't think Chip is going to be able to stand it. He's going crazy."

"For him it's a short trip," observed Rudy.

* * *

"Wow!" screamed Chip as Rudy came off the obstacle course well ahead of the rest of Cabin 13. "That must be a new camp record! Way to go, Miller! What a workout!" He turned to Frank. "Look at that! The kid didn't even work up a sweat! What an athlete!"

"Strange he should only show up now," said the head counsellor sourly.

* * *

"Did you see that forehand smash?" howled Chip as Rudy danced around the tennis court opposite Fred Baldwin, Algonkian's tennis instructor. "Miller's winning! He's beating Fred in straight sets!"

"Shut up, Chip!" panted Fred warningly.

* * *

"We've got nineteen now! Mark that down," Chip barked at Frank. "That Miller! He's scored twelve goals!"

"So far," said Frank dryly.

"You know, Chip," exclaimed Leo Martin, the opposing coach, "nobody scores twelve goals in field hockey! We haven't even got a point yet!"

Chip's answer was a joyous laugh. "Ha! Twenty to nothing! Mark that down!" He cupped his hand to his mouth. "Way to go, Miller!"

* * *

"Well, let's see," said Frank sarcastically, tallying up the track and field results for the day. "Miller took the hundred metre dash, and the three hundred metres was—ah, yes, Miller again. The long jump went to

Miller, as did the high jump and the triple jump. The fifty and two hundred metre hurdles—Miller won both. Ditto the shot-put, the discus and the javelin." He paused to glare at Chip. "And you say you didn't know?"

"Honest!" cried Chip. "How could I know? Until today he never played anything here! He's weird, that's all! And this is part of it!" His earnest face broke into a wide smile. "But gosh, can he ever hit a baseball!"

*　*　*

"Well," said Mike, tossing his last bag of garbage onto the heap, "I guess you've had quite a day."

"Yes," said Rudy. "And I don't intend to have another one like it ever again. I'm getting out of here tomorrow."

"Can I come along?" asked Mike. "I wasn't too thrilled with today either."

Rudy nodded. "If you like."

"It's a good thing you're leaving," said Mike. "Pretty soon the clones would start coming at you with trophies."

"I've got enough of those," replied Rudy grimly. "I keep them on some shelves in the garage. Of course, my parents already have a spot reserved for my future Olympic medals. Maybe I'll get them a moose head to fill the empty space."

"You're so good at everything," said Mike, his voice filled with awe, "and you still hate sports."

"With a passion," agreed Rudy emotionlessly.

"Well, then, Harold Greene is right," said Mike. "You are a nut." He grinned. "And I must be a nut too, because I think I understand."

* * *

"Hi, guys," said Chip, walking into the mess hall where the counsellors were meeting. "Sorry I'm late."

"Oh, that's quite all right," said Ralph Deacon sarcastically. "It gave us a few extra minutes to talk about poor you and your problem kid, Miller."

"What do you mean by that?" Chip demanded.

There was a babble of angry voices until Frank rapped on the table for silence. "The guys are pretty mad at you, Chip," he said.

"We figure you made awful fools of us. You practically begged us to force Miller to join the sports program, and then you sent him out there to wipe everyone else out. That's pretty underhanded. We're trying to promote good clean fun here."

Chip sat down wearily. "Look," he said, "for the last time, I didn't know anything about Miller being the world's greatest natural athlete. How could I? I couldn't get him to play anything."

"But he won everything, Chip!" cried Frank. "Even the lousy game of horseshoes after supper! You can't make me believe that anyone that good refuses to play sports!"

"Well, it's the truth, take it or leave it!" said Chip angrily. "And don't think I don't know what's really eating you guys. You're sore because my one kid made your whole cabins look sick. Well, I don't know if you noticed, but he made my cabin look sick too. And that's as much of a problem as anything else. Our guys'll never work up any team spirit with one kid doing it all. And besides, good or bad, Miller's got as much right to play as anyone else!"

There was low discontented mumbling.

"Okay," said Frank, "that's all for tonight. Let's sleep on it."

* * *

The beaver sniffed at the round white thing that had fallen from the sky that morning and lodged in his dam. What was it? He nudged it with his nose. It seemed harmless. Warily, he poked it aside. It rolled off the dam, landed in the creek with a plop and sank.

He settled himself down to rest. There was much work to do tomorrow. He hoped that no more strange things would come falling down from the sky.

7
Never once, before today

At three o'clock the next morning Rudy reached to the upper bunk and tapped Mike on the shoulder. "Wake up," he whispered.

Mike swung his legs over the side and jumped down lightly. "I wasn't sleeping."

The two boys dressed quickly and slipped out of Cabin 13, shutting the door gingerly behind them.

* * *

Chip had not gone to bed. Over-excited by the day's athletic victories and depressed by his treatment at the hands of his fellow counsellors, he had found it impossible to settle down. There was too much to think about. Now he was pacing along the waterfront, trying to sort himself out. Was he happy? Sad? Jubilant? Angry? In several hours of walking and mumbling to himself, he had come to only one conclusion: his life had been just dandy until the day Rudy Miller had walked into it. Now everything had turned to mud.

He was just about to start down the row of cabins to his own when he caught a glimpse of two shadowy figures running towards the dock. Mystified, he watched them scamper across the dock and jump into a small motor boat. He stared. Then suddenly a single thought entered his head.

"*Miller!*"

He began to run. He got to the dock just as the small boat roared away.

"Miller, you come back here!" Frantically he hurled himself into the nearest motor boat, a tiny outboard. He landed too close to the stern and the small craft, overbalanced, tipped straight up. Chip went down standing up, still yelling. Bubbles rose from where he had sunk out of sight.

"Rudy! Rudy, did you see that?" cried Mike, horrified.

"Yes." Rudy was already turning the boat around and kicking off his shoes, ready to go into the water. "Mike, take the wheel."

"Do we have to go back? Will we have to stay there?" Mike babbled, grasping the steering wheel.

"Of course we have to go back," said Rudy in disgust. "Do you want that big dumb clone on your conscience?" He jumped into the water.

Chip surfaced barely two metres away. "*Miller! What are you doing here?*"

"Rescuing you," replied Rudy calmly.

"I don't need any rescuing, but *you* will when I get through with you!"

"Gee," said Rudy, treading water, "you try to save a guy's life and that's the thanks you get."

Chip swam towards the dock. "Miller, get out of the water! Webster, is that you?"

"Yes," came a small voice.

"Well, dock that boat!" ordered Chip. He pulled

himself onto the dock. Rudy followed. They were met by an assortment of light sleepers from nearby cabins.

"What's going on here?" asked Ralph Deacon. "Hey, Chip, why are you all wet?"

"What do you want me to be when I come out of the lake?" Chip asked savagely. "*Dry?*"

Frank came rushing up. "What's happened here?"

Chip turned on him angrily. "My ringer, the guy I deliberately sprung on you to wipe you out on the playing fields, just tried to take off in a boat! What have you got to say to that?"

"If you hadn't fallen in, we would have made it too," Rudy commented mildly.

"Take off?" Frank repeated. "In a boat? Why?"

"Because I don't like it here," supplied Rudy. "As a matter of fact, I like it less every day."

"But—but you did so well yesterday!" stammered Frank.

"I don't play sports," explained Rudy.

Frank was struck dumb.

Chip turned to Mike. "And what about you, Webster? Where did you think you were going?"

Mike hung his head. "Home," he mumbled, pointing at Rudy, "with him."

"You two guys are just a little homesick," Frank managed feebly.

"Campsick," Rudy corrected. "As in sick of camp."

"This is serious," put in Ralph. "You're going to have to report it straight to Mr. Warden."

Rudy's eyes gleamed. "There's nothing straight about Mr. Warden."

Mike snickered nervously.

"First thing after breakfast," said Chip. "But right

now I'm freezing! Miller—Webster—march!"

"Aren't you going to chain our ankles together?" asked Rudy innocently.

"Shut up, Miller! You're in enough trouble!"

"If you get into too much trouble, do you get sent home?"

"Move!"

* * *

Right after breakfast Chip left Bunk 13 in Frank's charge and marched Rudy and Mike to the camp director's cottage. Mr. Warden met them at the door and showed them into the camp office. He seated them all in chairs opposite his desk.

"Well, now," he said sternly, "what's all this I hear about you two taking a boat without permission?"

"Actually, sir—" Chip tried to explain.

"Quiet, Chip," said Mr. Warden. "Now, listen, boys. This is Camp Algonkian Island. It was founded thirty-one years ago by my grandfather, Elias Warden, and in all that time not once, before today, has anyone taken a boat without permission."

"But, sir—" Chip interrupted. The director seemed to be missing the whole point in not seeing that Rudy and Mike had actually tried to run away.

"Chip, you will not interrupt me while I am speaking. Boys, do you know what the punishment is for taking a boat without permission?"

"Death?" asked Rudy innocently.

There was a strangled cough from Mike.

Mr. Warden chuckled forgivingly. "No, nothing so drastic as that," he said. "But I'm afraid I'll have to give you a good five days work detail. And I also insist that you each promise never to take a boat again without permission."

"I promise," chorused Rudy and Mike.

"Sir—" Chip put in desperately.

"Now, now, Chip," said the director reprovingly, "the boys are both sorry and they've both promised never to do it again."

Chip sighed. "Yes, sir. All right, guys, come on. We're late for letter writing."

Dear Mom and Dad, wrote Rudy. *How are you? I am okay. This certainly is a camp, all right. Only eight more days to visiting day. Your son, Rudy.*

"Miller, what's this?" bawled Chip, reading over Rudy's shoulder.

"My letter home," explained Rudy calmly.

"It's the exact same letter you wrote last time."

"No it isn't," said Rudy. "There were twelve days to visiting day then."

"Can't you think of anything better to write than that?"

"I tried to write an imaginative letter last time," said Rudy. "You wouldn't let me mail it."

"Yeah," said Chip, "but it's word for word."

"Except for the eight," said Rudy. "Anyway, I didn't think you'd want me to write about how you kicked in the cabin and broke the table and threw spaghetti at Harold Greene and jumped in the lake— twice."

"Never mind," sighed Chip. "This letter's good enough. All right, you guys! Time to play baseball! We're on a winning streak, you know!"

Rudy turned to Mike. "How about a little chess?"

"Sounds good to me," said Mike.

"There goes our winning streak," muttered Adam Willis.

Chip bit his lip to stifle a cry of protest. It seemed to him that forcing Miller to play sports had brought on his attempt to run away. Perhaps, if left alone, the boy would come to his senses.

"All right, you guys!" said Chip. He turned and bellowed, "Who's going to win?"

"They are!" chorused everyone.

"Awww," groaned Chip, "that's a terrible attitude! Miller, Webster, sure you won't change your minds? We can use you out there."

"No, thank you."

"Fine," said Chip painfully. "Come on, guys. Let's go."

* * *

"Boy," said Mike, pushing his pawn to king four, "what did you think of the lecture we got from the Warden this morning? He didn't seem to know we were trying to escape."

"And he didn't let His Cloneship tell him," Rudy added, moving his king's bishop aggressively.

Mike withdrew his queen's knight to safety. "He thought we just took a boat without permission."

"We did," said Rudy. "Old Elias must be spinning in his grave."

"But Chip *did* ruin our escape."

"Tomorrow morning we go again."

"Rudy," moaned Mike, advancing a rook, "isn't five days work detail enough?"

"It doesn't matter when you're not here to do it." Rudy brought out his queen.

"I don't think I want to try again tomorrow," said Mike with a worried frown. He moved his king defensively. "Couldn't we wait a day or two?"

"And stay here?" asked Rudy scornfully. "You stay. I'm going." He plunged his queen deep into Mike's shattered position. "Checkmate." He looked up at his opponent. "Your mind just isn't on the game, is it?"

Disgusted, Mike hurled a knight across the room. "Do you win at *everything?*"

"Yes," said Rudy sadly.

* * *

"This is the last of our two days work detail," grumbled Mike, pushing his wheelbarrow down the path to the dump. "Tomorrow we can start serving our five." He and Rudy had spent most of the day playing chess and lying by the creek listening to Rudy's radio.

"Tomorrow we do *not* start serving our five," said Rudy. "At least I don't. Tomorrow is the first day of the rest of my life as a free man." He paused. "Have you decided whether or not you're coming?"

Mike nodded vigorously. "I'm coming all right!" he exclaimed. "Did you see how mad everyone was at you at dinner? They got slaughtered because you didn't play—slaughtered at everything! And when they're mad at you, they're mad at me—guilt by association, I guess. Anyway, I sure don't want to stay here!"

"Chip hasn't yelled at me once today," observed Rudy, starting to dump his garbage bags. "Maybe he thinks a little loving kindness will stop me from wanting to escape." With athletic ease he tossed the last bag to the top of the heap. "Little does he know that nothing can stop me from wanting to escape from Alcatraz."

"Do you think they're going to make us play again?" asked Mike.

"They can try," said Rudy grimly. "Anyway, it's not important. We're not going to be here after tomorrow."

I've heard that before, Mike thought. But he did not dare say it aloud.

* * *

"Wow!" said Chip sarcastically as he walked into the counsellors' meeting that night. "That was a real dirty trick, Tyler, beating us nineteen to nothing at baseball. Almost as bad as you, Deacon, beating us twenty-one to nothing at soccer. They're real tricky, don't you think, Frank? Real tricky."

"Aw, come on, Chip, we're sorry about that," said Frank. "How were we to know? This Miller isn't your average guy."

"I'd think you'd have taken my word for it!" snapped Chip.

"You're just cranky because you fell in the lake," laughed Pierre. "Anyway, where *was* your boy wonder today?"

"He and his accomplice were playing chess while we were getting clobbered at baseball," sighed Chip. "And while we were getting smashed at soccer. And in the afternoon while we were getting wiped out on the track and pulverized in the swim races, they were resting in the woods, listening to the radio."

"I still say you should force him to play," said Frank. "He's the only real athlete you've got."

"Yeah, and what about our camp teams?" added Ralph, wide-eyed with eagerness. "With a guy like Miller on our teams we could clobber the whole north country. We're soon due to play Spruce Valley at baseball."

"And I've got to take a soccer team to Cedar Ridge," added Jack. "We could sure use Miller! I vote we force him."

"Nobody asked you," snapped Chip. "He's in *my* cabin. Last time we forced him to play he tried to run away the next morning. If you can convince him—bribe him, whatever—to play willingly, then fine. But nobody's going to force him. Understood?"

"But we could be the Ontario *champions*!" protested Frank. "We've *never* been the Ontario champions!"

"Tough," said Chip painfully. He would have given a lot to see Algonkian Island the Ontario champions. "The kid comes first. That's what we were taught, and that's what I'm going by."

"Can't we try?" whined Ralph.

"All you like," invited Chip. "But no threats."

* * *

The beaver was afraid. He had wasted half a day hiding when he should have been working. In the afternoon, two humans had appeared and settled themselves for a long time close to the dam. Their presence was menacing. But he must finish his dam and build his lodge—in spite of the humans and their noisy black box.

8
Flavour for the soup

On the stroke of four, Rudy reached into the upper bunk and shook Mike. "Departure time," he whispered.

With a low moan Mike jumped down and began struggling into his clothes. He mumbled, "I'm sure my outlook on Alcatraz would be much less severe if only I could get some sleep."

"Pretty soon you won't need an outlook on Alcatraz at all," Rudy whispered back. "It'll all be nothing but an unpleasant memory. Ready?"

Mike nodded. "Let's go."

They tiptoed towards the door and were just reaching for the doorknob when each was suddenly seized by his belt and hauled backwards into the counsellor's room.

Chip, his face flaming with anger, shut his door and turned on them. "*Miller!*" Although the counsellor was whispering, it sounded like shouting. "Where do you think you're going?"

"The dock, the mainland, and then home," Rudy replied calmly.

"What kind of a guy are you, Miller?" Chip fumed.

"I heard you promise Mr. Warden that you wouldn't take a boat without permission!"

"That's right, and I won't. But last night I asked Mike if I could take a boat and he said yes. So I have permission. And I gave him my permission to come along with me."

"*What?*" Chip was no longer whispering. "Don't you bandy words with me! You know darn well Mr. Warden meant official permission!"

"Oh," said Rudy, poker-faced. "It's a good thing you stopped us then. Old Elias would have been annoyed."

Mike snickered and, amazingly, so did Chip. But the counsellor's amusement soon passed. "Get back into bed, Miller! And you too, Webster! And another two days work detail for each of you! Now move!" He opened his door and pushed them out into the campers' section of the cabin.

"What's going on?" came a sleepy voice from an upper bunk.

"What are you doing up?" bellowed Chip. "Go to sleep, all of you!"

The last sound Rudy heard before he drifted off was Mike laughing into his pillow.

* * *

"Hey," said Chip, looking around table 13 at breakfast, "where are Miller and Webster?"

"Who cares?" sneered Harold Greene.

"The last I saw," said Adam, "they were down at the dock watching them load empty cartons on the supply boat."

With a scream of protest Chip jumped up, overturning the bench and sending five boys sprawling. "The supply boat? *Oh, no!*"

He tore out of the dining hall like a madman and thundered across the compound, shouting "*Stop!*" all the way. As his feet pounded onto the wood of the dock, a horrible sight met his eyes. There stood Frank, clipboard in hand, waving goodbye to the supply boat as it pulled away. "No! Stop it! Come back!"

"What's the matter, Chip?" asked Frank, bewildered. "What's wrong?"

Frank watched in horror as Chip hurled himself off the dock and began swimming madly after the boat. "Stop! Come back!"

"Stop!" shouted Frank. He wasn't sure why.

Dave came running up from the nearby swimming dock. "What's the matter? What's Chip doing?"

"I don't know." Frank shrugged. "He's trying to catch the supply boat for some reason."

Dave laughed. "Look at him floundering around out there! If he wanted to catch that boat, he should have sent Miller!"

"Miller! That's it!" Frank exclaimed. "Miller must be on that boat!" He ran to the end of the dock and jumped into a small motor boat. The little craft roared out after the supply boat, and with its superior speed, cut in front of it. Frank waved the driver back to the dock, then pulled up beside Chip and hauled him aboard. They roared back to the dock.

Chip jumped from one boat to the other. "*Miller!*" he howled, his eyes searching the stacked cartons. "You come out right now!" Arms flailing, he knocked over a large corrugated carton in the stern. There sat Rudy and Mike, blinking in the sudden sunlight. Chip loomed over them, furious and dripping wet.

"Oh, hi," said Rudy genially. "Has it been raining?"

"*Miller!* What are you two doing here?"

"I don't suppose you'd believe me if I said we were being kidnapped," suggested Rudy.

"All right, Miller!" said Chip through clenched teeth. "You're going to pay for this!"

"Work detail?" asked Rudy.

"*Work detail!*" bellowed Chip. "Five more days! And kitchen duty! Today and tomorrow! Now get off this boat! *Move!*"

As Chip was quick-marching Rudy and Mike off the boat towards the dining hall, Frank was running along beside him.

"Don't you think you're being a little hard on them?" he asked in an undertone. "I mean, if you've been punishing them a lot, maybe that's why they want to run away."

"Ha!" exclaimed Chip. "If this keeps up, the next person running away from here will be *me!*"

"I don't suppose he'd be willing to give us that in writing," Rudy commented to Mike.

"Can it, Miller!" snapped Chip. "Now both of you—get in there and grab some breakfast. And when you're finished, report to the kitchen. The staff will put you to work." He turned to Frank. "Maybe a little potato peeling will show him who's boss around here!"

* * *

"Why," said Rudy, scraping the abundant leftovers from a stack of plates, "don't they just take our food and throw it straight into the garbage? That would eliminate the middle man."

"That's enough out of you," growled the chief cook. "Keep working. The sooner you finish the work, the sooner you get out to join your cabin and have some fun."

Rudy looked at Mike. "We're in no hurry," he said.

"Well, we are," said another cook. "We're not going to stay here overtime on your account. We work hard, you know. It's not easy cooking for a bunch of kids who don't like anything."

"Maybe they'd like something if everything didn't look and taste like putty," commented Rudy mildly.

"Well, if you don't like it," howled the chief cook, "why don't you just take a boat and leave?"

Instantly Rudy began to scrape and stack dishes with model efficiency. Taking his cue from Rudy, although he wasn't quite sure why, Mike too began to work quickly. In five minutes they were finished. Rudy grabbed Mike by the arm and began dragging him across the compound towards the dock.

"Hey!" protested Mike. "Where are we going?"

"You heard the man," said Rudy. "He distinctly said we should take a boat and leave."

"But we can't!" cried Mike. "We promised not to take any more boats!"

"Without official permission," Rudy added. "But now we have official permission—from the chief cook himself."

"But—"

"Well, is it or is it not official permission?" Rudy asked defiantly.

"I don't know—" Mike began.

"Well," Rudy interrupted, "suit yourself. I'm going." He continued to run towards the dock.

"But they'll see us! They'll catch us!" Mike protested, keeping pace.

"Maybe," said Rudy. "And maybe not. There must be a dozen guys out there in boats. Maybe they won't notice us."

The two jumped into a motor boat. Rudy was just casting off when they heard the sound of running feet, and a familiar voice howled, "*Miller! You come back here!*"

Chip caught the mooring line just as the motor roared into action and the boat tore away from the dock. With a terrified howl the counsellor, still clutching the rope, flew in a three-metre arc through the air before belly-flopping with a huge splash into the water.

Rudy gunned the boat to full speed.

"Rudy, stop!" screamed Mike. "He's still back there! We're towing him!"

Rudy glanced quickly behind them. There was Chip, kicking up a spray like a cabin cruiser. Instantly he cut the motor. "That," he said in disgust, "is the only clone in the world who can water-ski on his face."

"What are we going to do?" gibbered Mike. "He's going to kill us!"

Chip swam up to the edge of the boat and climbed on board. "Take it back to the dock," he gasped. "Now!"

Obediently Rudy turned the boat around, steered it up to the dock and threw the rope to Frank, who had witnessed the incident and was grimly waiting.

"What's all this?" shouted the head counsellor.

"When Chip fell in the lake," explained Rudy, "we stopped our boat and came back to pick him up." It was, in essence, the truth, with a few important points left out.

Chip threw back his head and emitted a horrible roar. "You saw what happened!" he screamed at Frank.

"So did I," said Rudy. "Your take-off was great, but your landing was a little rough."

"Shut up, Miller!" cried Chip. "You're in big trouble now! You promised Mr. Warden and you promised me not to take a boat without permission!"

"I *had* permission," said Rudy earnestly. "Official permission."

"Yeah?" snarled Chip. "Who from?"

"The chief cook. He said if we didn't like it here we should take a boat and leave. And we don't like it here, so we took a boat and left. At least, we tried to." He eyed Chip accusingly.

"That's it, Miller! *That's it!* You know darn well that wasn't permission to take off. Nobody gets permission to take off. You are stuck here, Miller! Here! And me with you! You can either try to make the best of it and maybe have some fun, or you can be an idiot." He paused, gasping for breath. "We are not going to force you to play anything. You can sit around and *rot* for all we care. But you're staying put. Understood?"

"Yes," said Rudy, his face expressionless.

"And that goes double for you, Webster. You should know better than to follow Miller around. He's just getting you into trouble. Now both of you—five more days work detail. And two more kitchen duty. Right now you go back to the bunk. You're confined there until lunch."

Rudy and Mike scampered away in the direction of Cabin 13.

"Wow," exclaimed Mike as they threw open the door and rushed inside, "was he ever mad!"

Rudy draped himself across his bunk. "This is Camp Algonkian Island," he recited. "it was founded thirty-one years ago by Elias Warden, Bow Legs the First. It is presently under the regime of Bow Legs the Third. Never before, until today, has a clone flown that far or that high without permission."

Mike laughed. "Don't you mean official permission?"

"Official permission," Rudy amended. "How about a little chess?"

"Chess? Doesn't anything bother you?" asked Mike, still shaking from the events of the morning.

"No," said Rudy flatly.

They were just setting up the board when Chip, glowering like an avenging angel, appeared in the doorway. "All right, you two—get over to the kitchen. You're to help prepare and serve lunch. Move!" He disappeared.

Rudy put the chess board aside and went over to Harold Greene's suitcase. He reached inside and brought out a single white sock.

"What's that for?" asked Mike suspiciously.

"We're to help prepare lunch," explained Rudy. "I thought this would add a little flavour to the soup."

* * *

"Hold out your plate," said Rudy patiently from behind the lunch counter. "I'm not Rubber Man, you know." He slopped a generous portion of beef stew onto the first plate. "Next."

Farther up the counter Mike, his white apron spattered with green, was serving pea soup. His eyes darted nervously into each bowlful that he ladled out.

Along came Cabin 13 in the line. The boys self-consciously ignored Rudy and Mike, all except Harold Greene, who snickered and sneered at both of them.

"Well, Miller," said Chip, smiling broadly, "how do you like serving the food?"

"A lot better than I like eating it."

"Hey, you," snapped one of the cooks from the kitchen, "I don't want to hear any more cracks about the food!"

"We'll have to whisper from now on," said Rudy confidentially to Mike.

This time Mike did not laugh. He had turned deathly white. As the last few boys filed by, he leaned over to Rudy. "Rudy, we've got to get out of here!"

"Why?" asked Rudy, about to fill two plates of stew for himself and Mike.

"The sock!" gasped Mike in a high-pitched wheeze. "Chip got it! It went into Chip's bowl!"

Faint indications of a smile played about the corners of Rudy's mouth. "Fate," he said quietly.

"Let's get out of here!" Mike repeated.

"We can't," said Rudy. "We have orders to sit down and eat lunch with our bunk under our clone's watchful eye."

"But, Rudy—"

"And I don't want any soup, thank you."

Mike had to laugh. "Neither do I!"

They sat down at table 13 and began to eat.

Chip, who was a hearty eater, dipped his spoon vigorously into the soup. His eyes bulged as he came up with a long, green, dripping sweat sock.

"Hey! What's this?"

Still holding the spoon half a centimetre from his mouth, Chip surveyed table 13. "All right, who did it?"

Rudy looked up innocently. "Did what?"

"*Who put this sock in my soup?*"

There was dead silence.

"Well," suggested Rudy helpfully, "why don't you look at the label and see who it belongs to?"

Gingerly Chip wrung the soup out of the sock and turned the cuff inside-out. "Harold Greene," he read. "Greene, you did this!"

"I didn't!" squeaked Harold. "Honest!"

Chip looked down the table to where Mike was sitting, red as a beet, and Rudy was passively eating his stew. "Miller! *You* did it!"

"It was Miller! It was Miller!" piped Harold.

Rudy put down his fork and heaved a sigh. "Caught again."

Frank came over to table 13. "Chip, what's this about a dirty sock in the soup?"

"Clean sock," Rudy amended. "The food around here is bad enough without having to worry about dirt."

"That's enough out of you!" came a shout from the kitchen.

"Putting stuff in the food is very serious," said Frank. "We'd better take him to Mr. Warden."

"Marvellous," said Rudy evenly. "I haven't heard about old Elias for a whole day."

Frank and Chip looked at each other and grinned,

but their amusement died as abruptly as it had been born.

"Never mind Mr. Warden," said Chip. "I can handle this. Miller, you're confined to the cabin for the rest of the day except for kitchen duty at supper and work detail. You too, Webster. You were in on this."

Rudy shook his head sadly. "And all because I wanted to improve the taste of the soup."

"You shut up!" came another voice from the kitchen.

"And," said Chip, "that'll be another two days work detail for each of you."

"And he should have to wash my sock," put in Harold savagely.

"I don't do laundry," said Rudy.

*   *   *

"So," said Chip, sitting down wearily at the counsellors' meeting that evening, "they spent all day in the cabin, which is all they want to do anyway."

"That kid Miller," said Frank, shaking his head. "I just can't figure him out."

"Well, I know one thing," said Chip with conviction. "We can't let him out of our sight. Three times they were caught trying to run away today! Three times! And I'm sure he hasn't given up yet. One of us has to be with him at all times. And Webster is just as bad when he's with Miller, which is all the time."

"Hey," suggested Ralph, "why don't we separate them?"

"That's a great idea," said Frank. "Without Miller, Webster won't be any trouble at all."

"Without Miller," said Chip dreamily. "What a beautiful thought! But it can't be done. Miller and Webster like each other, and nobody else in camp can stand either one of them."

"Besides," nodded Frank in reluctant agreement, "they may not like it here, but it's still our job to see that they hate it the least."

The meeting was interrupted by the stormy entrance of the chief cook. "All right,' he demanded, "which one of you is the keeper of that guy Miller?"

"I am," admitted Chip sadly.

A piece of paper was thrust under his nose. Chip began to read: "*We the undersigned refuse to work in the Algonkian kitchen if Miller is going to be there.*"

"It's been signed by every member of the kitchen staff," pointed out the cook.

Chip sighed. "What exactly has he done?"

"He puts down the food all the time."

"Come off it," scoffed Frank. "You guys have worked in a camp long enough to have learned to ignore wisecracks about the food."

"I understand," put in Chip. "When it's Miller it's different. He's so—so *good* at it. I'd better take him and Webster off kitchen duty before we have a revolution."

"Oh, we don't mind Webster," said the cook. "Mind you, he laughs at all Miller's jokes—better take them both off. We'd sure appreciate it."

"That's okay," said Chip. "The only problem is that I've run out of ways to punish them. Anybody got any ideas?"

"How about putting them on work detail?" suggested Jack Tyler.

"I've lost count of their work details," admitted Chip. "For all I know they're on until Christmas!" He rested his chin on his palm. "Anyway, we've got to keep an eye on Miller. They said they're going to arts and crafts tomorrow right after breakfast. I'll see that they get there. Then it's up to you, Pierre."

"What," asked Pierre, "have I done to deserve that?"

"Just watch them," said Chip. "You're in charge of them until lunch."

* * *

The beaver was satisfied. The humans had been quiet today, and he had been able to accomplish a great deal of work on the dam. It was really taking shape now. He hoped he would have many more productive days like this one.

9
The great escape

"Hi there, Miller." Ralph Deacon, with an extravagant smile, inserted himself between Rudy and Mike at the breakfast table the next morning. "How goes it with you?"

Rudy raised expressionless eyes to the Cabin 3 counsellor, then turned back to his breakfast.

"Say," began Ralph, undaunted, as if a brilliant idea had suddenly occurred to him, "I'm making up an Algonkian Island all-star baseball team. In a couple of days the Spruce Valley team is coming here to play us. How would you like to be our pitcher?"

Rudy began methodically peeling an orange. "I don't play baseball," he said quietly.

"Sure you do," cried Ralph. "You're great at baseball!"

"I don't play it," said Rudy, even more quietly.

"All he plays is chess!" sneered Harold Greene.

"Shut up, Greene!" came from Chip at the head of the table.

Ralph's face brightened. "Chess, eh? I'm a pretty fair chess player myself. I'll make you a deal. Meet me at four this afternoon, in my room in Cabin 3. We'll have a game of chess. If I win, you play on my baseball team."

Rudy cocked his head, interested. "And if *I* win?"

"Well," said Ralph, "name it."

"I want to go home," said Rudy.

"Miller!" exclaimed Chip warningly.

"All right," said Rudy, "if I can't go home, then send *him* home." He pointed to Harold Greene.

"Nobody's going home," said Chip. "Ask for something realistic."

"How about making me camp director for a day?" suggested Rudy.

Ralph walked over to Chip and whispered, "What do you say?"

"Are you crazy?" exploded Chip. "You can't make Miller camp director for five minutes! He'll sink the island!"

"Oh, don't be silly!" whispered Ralph. "Schools these days are always coming out with 'principal for a day' contests, and small towns let kids play 'mayor for a day.' It's only a game. It won't mean anything. And Mr. Warden will be gone all day tomorrow. He doesn't even have to know about it."

"But I know Miller!" Chip insisted hoarsely. "His first official act will be to send himself home!"

"We'll stipulate that nobody's allowed to go home," argued Ralph. "Besides, there's no way he can beat me at chess! I'm a Class A player with an eighteen hundred rating! And what about my baseball team? Spruce Valley were last year's champions. They'll murder us if I don't have Miller. Come on, Chip. I'll clear it with Frank."

Chip sighed. "If Frank gives permission, then it's okay with me."

Ralph rushed across the mess hall and began whispering excitedly to the head counsellor.

After a heated discussion, Frank approached table 13. "All right, Miller," he said, "the deal's on. *But*—if you win, your term of office lasts only for tomorrow, after Mr. Warden leaves for the mainland. During that time you can't send yourself or anybody else home. And you're not allowed to damage camp property. No trenches, no fires, no bombs. Understood?"

"Agreed," said Rudy.

"Good!" said Ralph. "Four o'clock." He was jubilant.

Frank pulled Ralph aside. "If you lose . . . " he intoned warningly.

* * *

Chip marched up to the door of the arts and crafts building and ushered Rudy and Mike inside. "Here they are, Pierre," he said meaningfully. "They'll be here until lunch. Bring them to the mess hall at noon." He leaned over to Pierre and whispered, "And don't let them out of your sight for one second until then!"

Pierre grinned. "Don't worry," he promised. "They'll get busy on a project and it'll be noon before you know it. I hope."

Chip turned to Rudy. "I'll see you and Webster at lunch." He jogged off towards the soccer field.

"Well," said Pierre genially, "what have you got planned for today? Another *saleté*?"

"I don't think so," said Rudy. "Our last one wasn't really appreciated."

"Why don't you do some more woodworking?" suggested Pierre. "You could make nice tie racks for your dads."

Rudy shrugged affably. "Sounds okay. Would you please go and get us the materials?"

Pierre started off in the direction of the equipment storage room, then stopped short and chuckled inwardly. "Come along with me," he invited amiably.

"Oh, no thanks," said Rudy. "We'll wait here."

"Oh, I insist," said Pierre firmly. He was no longer smiling.

Rudy and Mike exchanged a knowing glance and meekly went along with Pierre to the materials room. Each selected some wood and a design sheet and sat down at the drawing table to plan his project. Keeping one watchful eye on Rudy and Mike, Pierre walked over to help some other boys who were doing leather work.

"I feel like a prisoner," whispered Mike angrily. "It looks like the clones are on us to stay. Chip delivers us here; Pierre has to escort us back to the mess hall. We aren't going to be allowed to go anywhere without some clone on our necks!"

"Well, that's to be expected." Rudy shrugged, sketching a design for his tie rack. "After all, we did try to escape several times yesterday. And this *is* Camp Algonkian Island—"

"Yes, yes, I know," interrupted Mike sourly. "Elias wouldn't have liked people escaping. But Rudy, don't you see we're worse off than we were before? We won't be able to breathe without a clone around to supervise it!"

Rudy's eyes gleamed. "But clones are human—in a

vague sort of way. And when Pierre goes to the wash station or something, he won't be able to take us with him. That's when we make our move."

"What move?" asked Mike suspiciously.

"Our move to get off this miserable rock," replied Rudy. "I don't know about you, but I'm still planning to go home."

"What about your chess game with Ralph?"

Rudy shrugged indifferently. "Ralph will get over his disappointment. Life goes on. I'm going to be long gone by four o'clock.

"Wishful thinking," said Mike. "We'd still have to take a boat, and that's impossible. We promised not to, and there's no getting around it this time."

"On the contrary," said Rudy. "Somewhere at the other side of this island there's a boat—our sailboat. We wouldn't be taking it—it's already been taken."

Mike held his head. "How do you know it's still there?"

"Simple. If it were adrift, someone would have found it. It has to be beached on the island, probably near where we landed that morning."

"Yeah," said Mike sarcastically. "We get in it and we sail away, and Pierre sounds the alarm. Then every clone in the place comes after us in the power boats. They'd overtake us in half a second!"

"But they don't know about our sailboat," Rudy explained patiently. "So they won't think to look on the other side of the island. They'll be waiting for us to make a break for the boats at the dock. Meanwhile, we just slip out the back way."

"But—what if Chip or someone sees us out of arts and crafts?" Mike protested.

"All we have to do is run to the woods," said Rudy. "Then they'll never find us." He looked long and hard at Mike, interpreting his nervous expression. "If you've got any thinking to do, do it now, because as soon as Pierre goes off somewhere I'm leaving."

"I'm going too," said Mike quickly.

Pierre walked over to inspect their drawings. "How are things coming along here?"

"Great," said Rudy enthusiastically. He added something to his diagram. "Do you think I could attach a dowel here and countersink a screw on the other side to keep it steady?"

"It's a good idea," nodded Pierre.

"And what about the wood?" added Rudy. "Do you think this piece would stain a nice dark walnut? I want it to match my folks' bedroom furniture."

Pierre nodded again. "If you sand it properly. What about yours, Webster?"

"I'm going to do mine just like his," stammered Mike nervously.

"That figures," said Pierre with a crooked smile.

Pierre walked back to help the leather-workers. Well, who would have thought it? Every counsellor in the camp was worrying about how to control Miller and here he was, happy as a lark, building a tie rack. He was good at woodworking, too, if the design meant anything. The kid just didn't like sports, that's all. But if they kept his hands and his mind busy, he wouldn't be any trouble at all.

In the distance he heard the sharp horn of the mail boat. The plans should be here—the ones he'd ordered from *U-Build Crafts*. There were all sorts of new woodworking ideas and he was anxious to see them.

He glanced around the room. All heads were down, and all hands busy. There was no point in waiting until lunch to see what the mail boat had brought.

"I'll be right back," he said to the boys, and added meaningfully, "*right* back." He dashed off in the direction of Mr. Warden's cottage, where the mail was taken to the camp office to be sorted.

Like a ferret Rudy stuck his head out of the arts and crafts doorway and looked around. "Now," he said softly, and took off for the woods.

Breathing a silent prayer, Mike ran after him. The two boys made it to the shade of the trees and kept on running.

*　*　*

The beaver was industriously gnawing at the base of a sapling which he planned to add to his dam. He was satisfied with himself. The dam was nearing completion. There had been no rain for a while, and his instinct told him he had several dry days left before a good one would come along to swell the creek and test his dam.

Suddenly the ground began to tremble beneath him. He looked up. Two humans were thundering through the woods directly towards him. Terrified, he scurried into the underbrush and watched with frightened eyes as the two stampeded by. One of them crashed headlong into the sapling he had been working on, and knocked it down. The human went sprawling.

*　*　*

"Are you all right?" asked Rudy, hauling Mike up off the ground.

Mike nodded breathlessly. "Let's keep going! We don't know where to find that boat!"

"Don't worry," said Rudy. "I've got a pretty good sense of direction."

"Oh, the orienteering champion too?"

Rudy glared at him. "Come on. And look where you're going this time."

*   *   *

"What do you *mean* you just went out to get the mail?" Chip shouted at Pierre. "I thought I told you not to leave them alone!"

"But they were busy. They were enjoying it." Pierre defended himself half-heartedly.

"I told you about Miller! I told you!" yelled Chip. "Okay, okay, we have to stay calm." He looked around desperately. "Frank. *Frank*!" He tore off in the direction of the baseball diamond, where the head counsellor was acting as scorekeeper. Pierre was right behind him.

"What is it this time?" asked Frank.

"Miller!" panted Chip. "Miller's gone! He and Webster escaped from arts and crafts!"

Frank blew two long blasts on his whistle to call the counsellors together. They converged from all directions—from the dock, the swimming area, the obstacle course, the track, the soccer field and several of the buildings. They all crowded around Frank.

"Okay—listen, all of you! Miller and his pal have disappeared. I want the dock sealed off and the entire compound searched. Anybody who finds them, or spots them, give three sharp blasts on the whistle. From now on, that's the Miller alarm. Now, scramble!" He turned to Chip. "Don't worry, Chip. They can't get far without a boat."

*   *   *

"Ah, here it is," said Rudy with satisfaction. "I knew it would be around here somewhere."

Aside from a few scrapes, the small craft was in perfect condition. It was keeled over among the bullrushes and beached in some gravelly sand. Rudy and Mike heaved it upright and pushed it into the water.

"Hop in," Rudy invited. "You hang onto the sail. I'll steer."

They boarded, and the little sailboat began to move slowly towards open water.

"They'll see us when we get round to the camp side of the island," agonized Mike.

"They shouldn't," said Rudy. "We'll make for a part of the mainland farther south than their landing dock, at the very edge of the camp view. The clones'll be watching the camp, not the water. We shouldn't have any trouble."

"Famous last words!" muttered Mike.

"Stop complaining and hang onto that sail. It's going to take us quite a while to get to the mainland."

*   *   *

Chip looked around the compound in despair. "It's been more than half an hour, Frank! Where can they be?"

"Some of the guys are looking in the woods," said Frank. "Miller and his pal are probably just hiding out so they can grab a boat tonight when we're asleep. We'll find them."

"You don't suppose they'd try to swim to the mainland?" asked Chip anxiously. "Miller could probably do it, you know—there and back!"

"Let's hope not," said Frank grimly. "Because I doubt if Webster could. Anyway, I don't think we have to worry about that. I don't think Miller is that stupid."

"What if they get hurt or lost?" asked Chip nervously. "They're only kids!"

"Don't worry," soothed Frank. "It's not your fault."

"I don't care whose fault it is," exploded Chip. "They could get *hurt!*"

Suddenly the air was shattered by three short whistle blasts.

"The dock!" exclaimed Chip. He and Frank tore off towards the waterfront. Other counsellors were also running in the direction of the alarm.

Dave, the swimming coach, was standing on the dock gazing out over the lake through high-powered binoculars.

"A sailboat," he said, handing the binoculars to Frank. "Way out there, almost beyond our view. A little farther south and we wouldn't be able to see it at all. It looks like ours—the one that's missing. And there's two people in it."

"Miller!" shouted Chip, grabbing the field glasses and almost removing Frank's nose in the process. "*You come back here!*"

"The boats," ordered Frank, rubbing his nose gingerly. "Let's get after them!" He and Chip jumped into a speedboat and roared off. Six counsellors leaped into the main launch and followed. Four more boats, each carrying two counsellors, joined the chase.

* * *

Rudy leaned back and tapped the tiller with great satisfaction. "Ten more minutes should have us on the mainland."

Mike grinned happily. "It looks as if we're going to make it this time."

Rudy nodded his agreement. "And so we bid an unfond farewell to exotic Alcatraz Island." He turned towards Algonkian. "Oh—maybe not."

"What? *What?*" Mike stared in horror. From the island a wall of white water was starting out in their direction. "Boats!" he squeaked.

"Man the oars," said Rudy calmly.

"Oars?" squealed Mike hysterically. "They've got powerboats!"

"Yes, but we've got a head start." Rudy grabbed an oar and began to paddle on one side of the boat. "Now stroke."

Mike took the other oar and worked it madly. "We're doomed!"

"We are if we go around in circles," said Rudy. "Paddle on the stroke . . . stroke . . . stroke . . . stroke . . ."

With their paddling assisting the sail, the small boat reached the mainland very quickly. By now the boys could hear the sound of the Algonkian Island armada coming after them. They could even see Chip in the lead boat, standing up and shaking his fist. They leaped out of their sailboat and scrambled up the grassy bank.

"What are we going to do? What are we going to do?" gibbered Mike.

"I don't know what you're going to do, but I'm going to run," replied Rudy. He took off through the woods.

"Wait for me!" shouted Mike, running after him.

* * *

"They're getting away! They're getting away!" howled Chip.

"Calm down," snapped Frank. "We'll be landing in a minute. They can't get far."

"Can't you make this thing go any faster?"

"No, I can't! Now sit down and shut up!"

The six boats soon landed and Frank addressed the counsellors. "All right, you guys, they went that way." He pointed up the bank where Rudy and Mike had disappeared. "They'll probably come to that town— Snow Hill. Let's move!"

Chip had already dashed up the bank and out of sight.

* * *

"A town," said Rudy. "Let's find a bus station."

"What about a telephone?" asked Mike, glancing nervously over his shoulder. "I thought the plan was to find a telephone and call our folks."

"No time. The clones can't be far behind us. We've got to keep moving."

"Where's the bus station, then?"

"It's got to be on this street," Rudy pointed out. "There are no other streets. Look, there's a cigar store. I'll go in and ask directions. You stay here and keep watch in the doorway."

"*Me?* Why me?" squealed Mike.

Rudy sighed. "Would you like to ask for directions and I'll wait outside?"

"No way!"

"Well, then . . . " Rudy opened the door of the small shop, stepped inside, made a fast turn and was outside like a shot, pulling Mike down the street.

"That was quick," said Mike. "Are we running to catch a bus?"

"Hardly," said Rudy mildly. "I couldn't go into the store. Chip was there."

"Oh, no!" moaned Mike. "Did he see you?"

"*Miller!*" howled a familiar voice behind them.

"He saw me," confirmed Rudy. "Quick. Down this alley." He pushed Mike ahead of him into the alley and headlong into Ralph Deacon, bowling him over. Rudy and Mike pulled away and took off in another direction.

Ralph, temporarily winded, sat up and blew three short blasts on his whistle.

Rudy and Mike pounded down the middle of the road as counsellors began to appear from all corners of Snow Hill.

"We're surrounded!" Mike panted hysterically.

"Run for the lumber yard," said Rudy calmly, pointing to a wide gate at the end of the street.

They made for the lumber yard, all sixteen counsellors in hot pursuit. Rudy vaulted over a pile of dressed lumber. Mike scrambled after him. "What good is this going to do?" he gasped. "Now we're trapped in the yard!"

"They'll all come in here to look for us," Rudy explained in a whisper, "and while they're looking we'll slip back out and get away. We don't have to stay here. There are other towns."

They heard Frank's voice calling, "They went in here! Search the place!" They could hear pounding footsteps as the crowd of counsellors began to spread out and search between the rows of lumber piled everywhere.

Mike gripped Rudy's arm hard enough to cut off the circulation. Frank had appeared to the left of them. The two fugitives wheeled to the right. There, in the narrow alleyway made by the piled-up wood, was Chip. They were trapped.

Rudy put his arms up in a gesture of surrender. "Comrade," he said resignedly. Mike stood trembling.

Chip and Frank ran up to them, each blowing three sharp whistle blasts to call the others.

"Put your hands down, Miller," said Frank in disgust. "Don't be an idiot!"

"*Miller*," bawled Chip, "this is the *end* of you!"

"For today," Rudy agreed.

"Did you really think you could get away?" asked Frank angrily.

"We almost did," said Rudy.

"Almost," echoed Mike forlornly.

"Shut up!" snapped Chip. "Just for this you've got ten more days work detail each!"

"And kitchen duty?" prompted Rudy in mock hope.

"You're off kitchen duty," grumbled Chip sourly.

"Enough chit-chat," snapped Frank. "Let's get back to the boats. And watch these two birds!"

"Birds?" repeated Rudy, highly insulted. "Birds?"

"Shut up, Miller!" growled Chip. "March!"

* * *

"Boy, oh boy, oh boy!" Ralph Deacon rubbed his hands together gleefully. "Is that Miller ever scared to play me at chess!"

"Yeah? Says who?" muttered Chip savagely.

"I figure he tried to run away just to avoid playing me," said Ralph. "Our chess game, remember? He must have heard about my rating and chickened out."

"Forget it," said Chip firmly. "No more chess for Miller. That's another one of his punishments."

"*What?* But my all-star baseball team—"

"Hang your all-star baseball team! It's me that has to deal with Miller, and I say no more chess!"

"You're missing the point!" insisted Ralph. "When he loses to me he'll have to play baseball, right? He won't be able to say we're pressuring him, because he agreed to the deal. What could be worse punishment? He *hates* it!"

Chip smiled dreamily. In his mind he had a picture of Miller on the baseball team. It was beautiful. Miller was so miserable. Chip frowned as the mental images changed. There was Miller, winning the chess game—Miller, camp director for a day. Oh, no! No, it could never happen. Ralph was twenty-three years old and had a high rating and Miller was just a kid. It was going to be all right.

* * *

"Checkmate," said Rudy quietly.

"Don't you think I know that?" cried Ralph Deacon, staring at the board incredulously.

Rudy stood up. "Thank you for the game," he said formally. "If you'll excuse me, it's almost dinner time, and right after that I have work detail—ten more days, you know."

"Um-hm," muttered Ralph weakly, still staring intently at the board. Miller had utterly destroyed him in less than twenty moves. And tomorrow Miller was going to be camp director. Frank and the guys were going to be mad enough to chew nails.

Rudy stepped outside of Cabin 3, where a large group of counsellors and a few campers were waiting.

"Tough luck, Miller," piped Chip. "This time you bit off more than you could chew."

Rudy frowned at him. "Show some respect, please," he said softly. "Tomorrow you'll be working for me."

"You *won?*" shouted Mike.

"He won!" groaned Chip.

"Oh, *no!*" thought Frank.

10
Attention, please!

Rudy Miller stood outside the mess hall shading his eyes from the early morning sun, watching the dock. Mr. Warden stepped into the launch and settled himself down. The line was cast off, the engine roared into life, and the silver boat pulled away.

A diabolical look, one he would never wear in public, spread itself over Rudy's normally expressionless features. He hefted the camp megaphone in his right hand, assumed his poker face, and entered the noisy mess hall.

"Your attention, please," he spoke into the megaphone. "This is your camp director speaking. I would just like to remind everybody that this is Camp Algonkian Island. There will be no activities today. Repeat, no activities."

A laughing cheer rose from the boys. Chip groaned and glared at Ralph Deacon, who winced visibly.

"And now," Rudy continued pleasantly, "I would like to appoint Mike Webster head counsellor."

"You've already got a head counsellor!" growled Frank.

"Yes, but he's been demoted," Rudy explained.

"Now, if I may continue—all punishment is hereby revoked. One of the counsellors will take out the garbage. Let's pick a number at random—uh, say, thirteen."

"Miller, you stop that!" shouted Chip, springing to his feet.

Rudy stiffened. "Never, since the days of our beloved founder, Elias Warden, has a counsellor disobeyed the camp director. Shape up, or you don't eat."

Chip, Frank and Ralph glared at Rudy. Everybody else laughed, some of the counsellors so hard that their heads were practically in their breakfasts.

"Quiet, please, I'm not finished." Rudy announced. "The 'no activities' rule, of course, applies to campers only. I have noted that the counsellors are in terrible physical condition. Accordingly, the counsellors' relay races will begin shortly after breakfast. This will be followed by the counsellors' obstacle course, the counsellors' shotput, the counsellors' swimming race, the counsellors' discus throw, the counsellors' ten-kilometre run, the counsellors' soccer game, field hockey game, baseball game, high jump and, if there is time, the counsellors' lunch."

By now the boys were in howling hysterics, but the counsellors were no longer amused.

"Miller, shut up!"

"This has gone far enough!"

"I'm not running ten kilometres on Miller's say-so!"

"He has no real authority!"

"All right!" announced Frank, rising to his feet. "That's enough. The game's over, Miller. You're not camp director any more."

"This is mutiny," warned Rudy calmly.

"Shut up, Miller!" said Chip furiously. "Get over here and give me that megaphone!"

"And about time too!" sneered Harold Greene.

Adam Willis leaped to his feet. "Now, just a minute!" he protested. "You guys made a deal, and Miller won fair and square! Just beause you don't like it, you can't weasle out!"

"It's not fair!" added someone from Cabin 15.

"He has a point there," said Pierre grudgingly.

"Whose side are you on?" snapped Chip.

"Well, you *did* make a deal," said Pierre lamely.

"If you're quite finished," said Rudy, "we can do this the democratic way. Who in this room believes in the concept of freedom and justice and wants me to serve my rightful term as camp director?"

"*We do!*" Most of the campers' hands went up, accompanied by wild yelling, cheering and stamping.

"Practically unanimous," said Rudy. "Now, as I was saying, all campers must rest and relax today. If you need something, send your counsellor for it. They are, after all, here at your service. There will be numerous announcements made as the day progresses. That will be all for now."

He got a tremendous cheer.

* * *

"When I blow this whistle," said Rudy into the megaphone, "the first counsellor on each team tucks the grapefruit under his chin, puts the sack on his feet and jumps over to that line of trees and back. Then he passes the grapefruit over to the next person—without using his hands. If he drops it, the whole team has to do ten push-ups each before continuing. The first team finished gets ribbons, which they may wear all day. Head counsellor Webster will be the judge."

Rudy blew the whistle and then blew it again. "Stop, stop. False start."

Chip was already lying on the ground, his feet tangled in the sack, a crushed grapefruit under his body.

"Team four, ten push-ups," Rudy ordered. "Frank, go and get another grapefruit, please."

"This day won't last forever!" said Frank warningly. He trotted off towards the kitchen.

* * *

"A treat today," announced Rudy. "Instead of having you run the old obstacle course, I've made up a new one for you."

Ralph wrung the grapefruit juice out of the front of his shirt.

The counsellors were a bedraggled sight. Chip, more dead than alive, had actually run into a tree. Frank's team had accumulated fifty push-ups. Jack Tyler had fallen so many times that he was dirt from head to toe. The only counsellors who wore smiles were Pierre and his team. They had won the relay race and now sported bright blue first-place ribbons.

"Here's what you do," instructed Rudy. "Everybody get a partner. First you run to where the jump ropes are and skip ten times. Then over to the sand pit, which you slither through snake-fashion. Then you somersault over to that tree, and hop on one foot over to the vaulting horse, which you get over any way you can. Then you leap over the wading pool and run to the baseball diamond, where you crab-walk around the bases. Then you climb through the tunnel and run over to where head counsellor Webster is waiting to check in your time. Have you got all that?"

A loud babble of protest exploded from the counsellors.

"What are the partners for?" asked Jack Tyler suspiciously.

"Oh, yes," said Rudy. "Didn't I mention it? This is all to be done three-legged with your partner."

"What?" cried Frank. "You mean tied together? Like a three-legged race?"

"Exactly," said Rudy.

Chip nudged Frank. "Why do we have to let him push us around like this?"

"Because if we don't," said Frank, "we come off looking bad to the rest of the kids. Besides, when you come right down to it, Ralph almost dragged Miller into this deal. If you want to kill somebody, try Ralph!"

"Come on, you guys," said Rudy. "There's ribbons in it for the three best times. And the worst three get ten push-ups. Line up. First two pairs."

Chip and Frank lined up beside Pierre and his partner. Rudy blew the whistle. Pierre and his partner took off in a shambling gait toward the jump ropes. Chip and Frank took two steps and fell over.

"Stop it, you klutz!" howled Frank. "That's my leg you're ripping out!" The two began to writhe and struggle.

"Get up, Chip! Get up!" cheered the boys of Cabin 13.

Slowly and painstakingly, Chip and Frank managed to get themselves upright. They began to shuffle off after the first pair, gradually getting the hang of running tied together. Soon they were hopelessly entangled in the skipping ropes. Meanwhile, Pierre and his partner were already somersaulting after their crawl through the sand.

"It's amazing," reflected Rudy philosophically. "Some people are natural-born athletes." In the distance, Chip and Frank fell over again. "And some people aren't."

* * *

"Okay," said Rudy, "your attention, please. Because of this morning's strenuous activities, I have decided to cancel the ten-kilometre run."

"And a good thing too!" growled Frank, flipping his wet hair back off his forehead. He and Chip had failed to clear the wading pool

"Instead," Rudy went on, "I would like everyone to gather in the woods by the creek."

"What for?" muttered Chip, trying to wring the water out of his shorts.

"The tug of war," explained Rudy as he led the march towards the woods. "All partners from the last event break up and go to opposite sides of the creek. Head counsellor Webster will, of course, be judge."

As the two teams lined up, with the rope strung across the creek, the counsellors surveyed the scene distastefully. Miller had chosen the spot well. The winners were going to get ribbons, and the losers were going to get wet.

"When I blow the whistle," announced Rudy, "you all start pulling. Are the instructions perfectly clear?"

"Get on with it," muttered Frank absently. He was staring across the creek at his opponents with a look of determination on his face.

Rudy blew his whistle and Frank's team effortlessly pulled Chip's team right off the bank and into the creek. The cheering from the campers and the winning counsellors was deafening.

Rudy blew his whistle for order. "Head counsellor Webster, your decision."

"I think those guys won," stammered Mike, pointing at Frank and his team.

From his pocket Rudy produced a handful of blue ribbons and began to distribute them among the winners.

Chip waded out of the creek and glared at Frank, who was proudly displaying his ribbon and laughing at the spectacle of half his staff floundering about in the creek. Enraged, Chip reached out, closed his big hand on Frank's ankle and heaved. Feet first, Frank hit the water.

"What did you do that for?" he spluttered.

In answer Chip placed his hand on the top of Frank's head and pushed him under water. As if on cue, all the winners jumped in and went after the losers. Chip and Frank were splashing violently at each other. In a matter of seconds the creek was a boiling torrent of rollicking, laughing bodies. On the shore, the campers cheered themselves hoarse.

Rudy blew the whistle and the brawl ceased. One by one the counsellors crawled out of the water and stood dripping and gasping on the bank.

"This is Camp Algonkian Island," began Rudy sternly. "Whatever that outburst was, I'm sure that it hasn't happened since the days of Elias. I expect better than this from my staff. Watch it, or you don't eat.

And speaking of eating, it's time for lunch. Everyone go clean up."

As they walked back towards the compound, Mike caught up to Rudy. "You know," he said nervously, "tomorrow the clones are going to nail you to the wall and me to you!"

"In that case," replied Rudy, "we'll just have to leave, won't we?"

Mike's eyes widened. "I heard you promise Frank that nobody goes home!"

"Right," said Rudy. "That was for today. I never said anything about tomorrow."

Mike's heart sank.

*   *   *

"Your attention, please," announced Rudy over the megaphone. Everyone was just coming to the end of lunch. "This is your camp director speaking. This afternoon all campers and counsellors will take part in the first annual Elias Warden Memorial Scavenger Hunt. Head counsellor Webster is now handing out the mimeographed sheets of what you are to retrieve. When you are finished, gather outside my office to have your things checked out. There are ribbons in it for the best collectors. The judge, as always, will be head counsellor Webster."

"And what will you be doing, oh imperious leader?" asked Frank sarcastically, taking a scavenger sheet from Mike.

Rudy sighed. "Head counsellor Webster and myself have heaps of paperwork to be taken care of," he said wearily. "We'll be in my office."

"I'm going to be there, Miller," said Frank through

clenched teeth. "When Mr. Warden's away, that office is my responsibility."

"When the camp director is away," corrected Rudy. "However, the camp director is here—me. And when I'm away, my duties are taken over by the head counsellor—him." He pointed to Mike.

"I know what he's up to," piped up Harold Greene. "He just wants to get to the office phone to call his parents to come and get him!"

"Shut up, you twit!" snapped Mike.

"Greene, you're on work detail tonight," said Rudy briskly.

"I don't have to listen to you!" sneered Harold.

"Yes you do!" shouted Adam Willis. "Miller is camp director today and he's the boss! Isn't that right, Chip?"

"Yeah," mumbled Chip unhappily.

"All right, everyone," Rudy announced. "Into the woods. Pair up if you like. Happy hunting."

He and Mike walked towards the camp director's cottage. Frank followed.

*　*　*

"Soon today will be over," breathed Chip to Pierre, his partner. "Miller's game will finish, and mine will start. I'll have his hide for this!"

Pierre laughed. "I don't know, Chip. I think Miller's just what this place needs. Listen to what's going on." All around them the woods rang with shouts and laughter from campers and counsellors alike. "I've never seen camp spirit like this. And the kid is so funny! I knew it the minute he pulled that *saleté* bit!" He chuckled at the mere memory.

"I didn't find it funny," grumbled Chip.

"That's because the joke was on you," said Pierre. "Now, come on. Get into the spirit of the thing. What's the first item on the list?"

Chip looked, then stared. "*A brontosaurus rib*," he read. "You see? Miller's crazy! I told you!"

"What a sense of humour!" marvelled Pierre. "All right, let's fight fire with fire. We'll substitute a chicken bone from the dump." He slapped the bewildered Chip on the shoulder. "Let's see what our friend Miller has to say to that."

Chip grinned grudgingly.

* * *

"Get away from that phone!" snapped Frank suddenly. "You're not to touch it!"

"What if it rings?" asked Rudy.

"Then answer it," said Frank. "But I want you to promise that you won't make any calls yourselves."

"I promise," chorused Rudy and Mike.

"Ah," said Rudy, looking around the office, "time to examine the records." He pulled open a filing cabinet.

"Get out of there, Miller!" snapped Frank. "Those are confidential records on all the campers."

"Well, we can certainly see our own," said Rudy, flipping through the folders. "Here it is—*Miller, Rudy*." He began to read silently. "It says here that I'm a homesick troublemaker who won't take part in anything. Not very flattering, but at least Chip got the last part right."

Mike found his own folder and pulled out the evaluation sheet. "Hey, mine's blank!"

Rudy produced a pen. "Well, we'll soon remedy that." Before Frank could stop him, he had scrawled *Chooses friends well* on Mike's report and initialed it *R.M.*

"Miller, you put those files back and close that drawer," shouted Frank. "Come sit down at the desk and stay out of trouble!"

* * *

"I wonder if this is a eucalyptus tree," said Joey Peters to his partner, Adam Willis. "We're supposed to bring back eucalyptus bark."

"It's just plain elm," replied Adam.

"We'll take it anyway," decided Joey, stripping some bark from the trunk. "Miller won't know the difference."

Adam laughed. "The counsellors underestimated Miller too, and now he's the camp director."

"I wish he was camp director all the time," said Joey. "I've never laughed so much in my life! When Chip and Frank took off on Miller's obstacle course I thought I'd die!"

* * *

"This," said Pierre to Chip, "is the closest thing to a moon rock you're going to find on Earth."

"Good," said Chip. "We'll use it. I can't wait to see the look on Miller's face when we give him a taste of his own medicine with this stuff."

"What's next on the list?" asked Pierre.

Chip made a face. *"Pure mineral water.* Now, where are we going to find pure mineral water?"

"Follow me," said Pierre, starting to walk purposefully towards the creek. He dipped a jar into the creek and brought it up again.

"Behold—water." He picked up a rock from the bank.

"Behold—mineral." He dropped the rock into the jar. "Presto—mineral water."

"It's not pure," protested Chip.

"Quit spoiling it or I'll get another partner," said Pierre. "This scavenger hunt is supposed to be for fun."

"Miller doesn't believe in fun," growled Chip. "Ask him."

"You know what your trouble is?" said Pierre. "You're like Mr. Warden. You don't like kids."

"I like kids," argued Chip. "But Miller isn't a kid."

"Forget it," said Pierre. "What's next?"

Chip winced. *"Nuclear waste."*

* * *

The telephone in Mr. Warden's office rang. Rudy leaned back in the swivel chair, put his feet up on the desk and reached for the receiver, beating Frank to it by half a second.

"Good afternoon. Camp Algonkian Island. R. Miller, Director, speaking. How may I help you? . . . Ah, yes, the order for volleyballs. I remember it well . . . Ten? Oh no, I must have left off a couple of zeros . . . Yes, make that a thousand. We play a lot of volleyball up here. Why, just last week—"

"Miller, give me that!" Frank grabbed the receiver from Rudy's hand. "Hello, this is Frank. Hello? . . . Hello?" His face fell. "He hung up. Miller, if a thousand volleyballs arrive here, you're dead!"

"This is Camp Algonkian Island, soon to be famous

for its volleyball program," deadpanned Rudy. "Never before, since the days of Elias, has anyone threatened the life of the camp director."

Lips twitching, Frank stared at him, and then burst into laughter. "Don't let Mr. Warden hear your Elias jokes, Miller. And no more talking on the telephone." He glared at Mike. "Stop that snickering, Webster. You may be head counsellor, but tomorrow I'll have my job back!"

"No wonder Mr. Warden's always so cranky," said Rudy. "You never let him have any fun."

* * *

"Did you guys find anything?" asked Brian Meadows as he and his two partners came upon Adam and Joey in the woods.

"Nah," said Joey. "We're not doing very well. We missed the nuclear waste and the brontosaurus rib, and we faked the eucalyptus bark and the trilobite fossil."

"We got the pterodactyl nest," announced Brian proudly.

"So what?" said Adam. "We got the man-eating plant." He reached into his bag and pulled out a wilted dandelion.

"That's as authentic as our pterodactyl nest," agreed Brian, and they continued on their separate ways.

* * *

"What are you getting in the kitchen?" called Chip to Pierre, who had gone into the mess hall.

Pierre came out carrying two ice cubes in a paper cup. "The iceberg," he grinned. "That's everything now. Let's go get our ribbons."

With Chip carrying the carton containing their finds, they walked across the compound towards the director's cottage. A large crowd was already gathered, laughing and talking amid bags and boxes of scavenger hunt treasure.

Rudy, Mike and Frank appeared on the veranda. The campers began to cheer wildly.

"What are they yelling about?" asked Chip peevishly.

"They're cheering Miller," explained Pierre patiently. "They've had a real good day."

Rudy spoke into the megaphone. "It is now time for the judging of the first annual Elias Warden Memorial Scavenger Hunt. Raise your hand if you got the iceberg."

Pierre kicked Chip in the back of the leg, causing him to emit a startled yell.

"Chip—what a surprise," said Rudy. "Come on up. Let's see your iceberg."

Defiantly Chip stepped up onto the veranda and held out the cup containing the rapidly dwindling ice cubes. "It melted a little while we were getting it here."

"Understandable," said Rudy. "A very fine specimen indeed." He presented a shocked Chip with a blue ribbon and shook his hand solemnly. "Congratulations."

Amid applause, and beaming with amusement and pleasure, Chip walked back to Pierre.

"Now," said Rudy, "who got the eucalyptus bark?"

"We did!" piped Joey, running to the veranda and dragging Adam with him. "Here." He held out the bark.

"This is a fraud," said Rudy disapprovingly. He sniffed at the bark. "It's obviously elm."

"See?" laughed Adam. "He knows everything!"

Rudy handed a white third-place ribbon to Adam. "For a lesson well learned," he said.

Pierre earned a second-place red ribbon for his brontosaurus rib, as did Ralph Deacon for his plastic bagful of mud labelled *Nuclear Waste.* Joey redeemed himself by winning a first for the man-eating dandelion, and the pterodactyl nest earned a third for Brian Meadows. Jack Tyler got a first prize and the loudest cheer of the day when he submitted Leo Martin, counsellor of Cabin 15, as a genuine Neanderthal man. Chip and Pierre picked up a third for the mineral water. Five boys from Cabin 19 were awarded blue ribbons for their stalactite, which had taken them all afternoon to carve. Assorted prehistoric fossils, rare stones and natural phenomena were all justly rewarded.

By the time the awards broke up, it was supper time.

* * *

"Your attention, please. This is your camp director speaking." There was an enormous cheer from all the campers, as well as stamping of feet and banging on plates. "Tonight," Rudy went on after the rumpus had died down, "the counsellors' tag championships will take place. We'll have to pick a number to be 'it' first —uh, say, thirteen."

At table 13, Chip shook his head resignedly, but he was smiling.

"Head counsellor Webster will, of course, be referee," Rudy continued.

"After that, the counsellors will entertain by singing the 'Anvil Chorus' from *Il Trovatore* by Giuseppe Verdi."

There was a hoot of laughter from the counsellors.

"By then, Mr. Warden will be back to relieve me of my duties."

There were loud hisses, boos and groans at this announcement.

"At that time also," Rudy added, "Frank will resume his duties as head counsellor."

There were more boos, to which Frank stood up and took an elaborate bow.

"On a completely serious note," said Rudy, his face growing solemn, "I feel that Elias would have been proud of all of us today." He handed the megaphone to Mike for comment.

"Uh—yeah," stammered Mike. "Me too."

There was tremendous laughter and applause.

* * *

"*Tag!*" bellowed Chip, slapping Pierre on the back. "You're 'it'!"

Pierre took off after Ralph Deacon, who dodged frantically and ran screaming towards the dock.

The counsellors had already been at it for forty-five minutes, and all the campers were frolicking around with them. Everyone, except Rudy and Mike, was completely covered in dirt. The administrators, in their last hours of office, were seated on a bench at the centre of the compound, watching the game.

"Look at those clones," marvelled Mike. "It's hard

to believe. What's going to happen if the Warden walks in on this?"

Rudy shrugged indifferently. "What are you worried about? You're not the head counsellor. Frank is."

Mike laughed. "You really put it to them today. But tomorrow . . ."

"And that prospect constitutes grounds for departure," said Rudy.

Their attention returned to the tag championship.

"Ha!" shouted Frank. "You're 'it'!"

"I am not!" screamed Jack Tyler. "You didn't touch me!"

"I did so!"

"You did not!"

"Webster," called Chip, "you're the referee! What's the decision?"

"No tag," gulped Mike.

"*No tag?*" cried Frank. "What do you mean no tag?" He stuck out his foot and tripped Jack, who fell over, pulling Chip down with him.

"You did that on purpose!" stormed Jack.

"Darn right!" grinned Frank.

Chip laughed diabolically and knocked Frank down. In a matter of seconds all the counsellors had waded joyfully into the fray. The campers crowded around in a great circle, cheering.

There were two long whistle blasts, the signal used to summon the counsellors. Everyone jumped up and looked at Rudy, who pointed behind them. Slowly, agonizingly slowly, everyone turned. There, staring at them in open-mouthed disbelief, was Mr. Warden.

Helpfully, Rudy rushed over and handed the megaphone to the camp director.

"This is Camp Algonkian Island," Mr. Warden began slowly. He ignored the roar of laughter and continued, "It was founded thirty-one years ago by my grandfather, Elias Warden. Never before has the entire staff gone completely insane!"

"Shape up or you don't eat," whispered Rudy to Mike.

As always, Mike started the laughter. It spread like a virus through the ranks of the campers and grew until everyone, including the counsellors, was slapping knees, holding sides and laughing uproariously. Only Rudy and the camp director were in control of themselves.

Oh well, thought Mr. Warden, after all this is Camp Algonkian Island, where everyone is supposed to have a wonderful time. No harm done—I guess.

* * *

The beaver lay sleepless and trembling. Everything had been going along so well until today. But today humans had been everywhere, hundreds of them. Twice he had been swamped trying to protect the dam. Fortunately they had done little damage, but if they were constantly interrupting him, he would *never* finish his dam!

11
Name, rank and serial number

"Miller," began Jack Tyler uneasily at the breakfast table the next morning, "I'm making up the all-star soccer team to take over to Cedar Ridge tomorrow. You wouldn't want to join, would you?"

"Sure," said Rudy amiably. "Why not?"

Mike choked on his milk.

Chip dropped his fork with a clatter.

Jack's eyebrows shot all the way up to his hairline. "Yeah?"

"If Mike can come," stipulated Rudy.

"Oh—yeah. Yeah, sure," stammered Jack. "Mike who?"

"Former head counsellor Webster," said Rudy.

"Sure. No problem." Jack didn't particularly want Mike on the team, but Miller would make up for it. The way he played soccer, Miller would make up for everybody.

"I thought you didn't play soccer," sneered Harold Greene.

"Shut up!" snapped Mike. "Hey, Rudy," he whispered, "I thought you didn't play soccer."

"I don't," whispered Rudy in reply.

"So why did you volunteer to play?" asked Mike, bewildered.

Rudy's eyes gleamed. "I'll explain it later."

* * *

"Ralph, you poor unfortunate sap!" gloated Jack Tyler, watching the baseball game between the Algonkian all-stars and the visting team from Spruce Valley. "If you were a better chess player, you'd be winning this game."

"Your turn will come," muttered Ralph darkly, throwing his hat in the dirt and stomping on it as Spruce Valley scored yet another run. "Tomorrow, in fact, when Cedar Ridge pulverizes you."

"Don't be too sure," said Jack. "We've got a pretty good team this year and"—he paused for effect— "Miller's playing."

"*What?* How did you do that? What did you promise him?"

"Nothing," said Jack airily. "I just asked him to play and he said sure."

"But he didn't want to play baseball," protested Ralph in agony. "Why didn't he want to play on *my* team?"

"Who knows?" said Jack. "And who cares? I'm not one to look a gift horse in the mouth. He's going to play, and we're going to win."

The crack of a bat signified another hit for Spruce Valley.

"Congratulations," moaned Ralph, holding his head.

* * *

"Well?" demanded Mike as he and Rudy settled down in arts and crafts to work on their tie racks. He looked around to make sure that Pierre was out of earshot. "What's the big idea? Why did you agree to play for the soccer team? And why on earth did you volunteer *me?* I *hate* soccer!"

"Think," said Rudy with great relish. "Tomorrow, as members of the Alcatraz all-star soccer team, we are going to Cedar Ridge. Cedar Ridge is on the mainland. Presto. Opportunity knocks."

"We're going to escape in the middle of a soccer game?" asked Mike incredulously.

"Shhh. Yes," said Rudy. "On the way there, we'll pick out a meeting place. Then, during the game, we'll find some way to take off."

"What's the meeting place for?" asked Mike anxiously.

"In case we get separated," Rudy explained. "It'll probably work best if only one of us takes off first. Then, while the clones are looking for the first guy, the other guy runs off in the confusion. Then we meet and go home. Simple?"

Mike laughed nervously. "And if we're caught?"

Rudy shrugged. "They'll haul us back the way they always do, and we'll lug a little more garbage."

Pierre strolled over to them. "Hi. How are the tie racks coming?"

Rudy held up his untouched pieces of wood. "How do you like it so far?"

Pierre laughed. "You know, I expect better than that from the former camp director"—his glance took in Mike—"and his chief exec."

Rudy raised his eyebrows. "*I* expect more patience

133

and understanding from a man who won so many ribbons yesterday."

Pierre reached into his pocket. "Seven, to be exact. Say, Miller, I just heard that you're going to play for the soccer team. Is it true?"

"I have no privacy," Rudy complained.

"Then you're playing?" repeated Pierre.

"Yes."

"That's just great. I'm glad to hear it. Okay, don't let me disturb you. Keep working on the old tie racks. And tomorrow you show Cedar Ridge what it's all about."

"Oh, we intend to," said Rudy earnestly.

* * *

The beaver was having a good day. He had not been disturbed at all. The dam was nearing completion, rising strong and firm above the water level. Soon he would finish and the stream would widen into the pond he needed. He stopped in his labours and sniffed the air. It was still a good few days before the rain would come. And when it did come, he would be ready.

* * *

"Congratulations to *us*!" exclaimed Frank, waving his arms in victory among the rest of the counsellors at that night's meeting. "We have *done it*! We have made a camper out of Rudy Miller!"

"We have indeed," agreed Jack Tyler jubilantly. "The impossible has been done. If we could only explain it to Mr. Warden, I'm pretty sure an accomplishment like this would qualify us for a raise!"

"I should get the raise," put in Chip. "I took all the lumps."

"No, I should get the raise," muttered Ralph. "It was my baseball team that was sacrificed. Why couldn't you have made a camper out of him a day earlier?"

"We couldn't have done it without you, Ralphie-boy," laughed Frank. "It was your great talent as a chess player that brought it all about."

"Less than twenty moves," mourned Ralph. "That kid plays chess like Bobby Fischer!"

"And soccer like Pele," crowed Jack, anticipating tomorrow.

"And he runs like Henry Rono," added Chip, breaking into a broad grin. "We've got the intercamp track meet coming up next week."

"I wish we had some champagne," said Frank wistfully. "We could toast Algonkian, the new Ontario champions—at everything!"

"Except baseball," added Ralph sourly. "We were eliminated today, as you might have guessed."

"I'm wondering," said Pierre thoughtfully, "what would make a kid like Miller have such a change of heart."

"Oh, that's easy," said Frank. "Yesterday did it. Miller had a ball, and so did all the other guys. And so did we, for that matter."

"Hey, Frank," said Leo Martin, "did Mr. Warden give you any flak about yesterday?"

"No," laughed Frank. "A couple of times he looked as if he wanted to ask a question or two, but then he thought better of it. I don't think he wants to know, and I sure don't want to tell him. He wouldn't understand anyway."

"I want to go to the soccer match tomorrow," said Chip, "and watch Miller crush Cedar Ridge. Pierre, how about looking after my cabin for the day?"

"Well, I thought I'd go to the soccer game—" began Pierre.

"No fair!" yelled Dave. "I never get off the island! This time it's my turn!"

"No chance!" snapped Ralph. "My baseball team was sacrificed! The least you can do is let me go along on the trip to Cedar Ridge!"

The meeting became a babble of protest.

"I know," announced Chip. "We'll get Miller to pick a number at random—uh, say, thirteen."

"We'll draw lots," decided Frank. "That's the only square way."

*　*　*

Early the next afternoon the Camp Algonkian bus pulled up in front of a huge sign that read *Welcome to Camp Cedar Ridge, the Funshine Place*.

All camps looked alike to Mike Webster, and Cedar Ridge was no exception. There were the usual cabins, buildings and athletic facilities just like those at Algonkian. There was the 'you *must* have fun' atmosphere, although in this place it was probably 'funshine.' Even the counsellors looked and dressed the same.

"All cloned from the same master cell," commented Rudy to Mike. "I can hardly wait to see the camp director's legs."

The boys had been travelling for over an hour. They had left Algonkian Island by launch at one o'clock. A bus had been waiting for them at the mainland receiving dock, and they had driven about fifty kilometres, according to Rudy's calculations, in a south-easterly direction.

"Look," whispered Rudy as the team rattled off the bus, "do you see that big road sign down there around that bend? The woods are right up to the highway at that point. We'll meet just inside the woods by that sign. Got it?"

"Yeah, but how do we get there?" squeaked Mike.

"I'll figure that out when I see the soccer field," said Rudy.

"All right!" chirped Jack, "who's going to win?"

"We are!" cheered the Algonkian boys.

Chip, who had picked the longest straw at yesterday's counsellors' meeting and was convinced that his bad luck was changing, placed a large, meaty hand on Rudy's slender shoulder. "I'm expecting great things from you out there, Miller. I'm really glad you got smart and joined the team."

"I'm glad too," said Rudy, poker-faced.

A Cedar Ridge counsellor, the image of Frank, jogged up to greet them. "Hi there, Jack. Back for more?"

"We'll see," said Jack smugly.

"Come on, you guys! Let's move!" bellowed Chip, and the team trotted off towards the soccer field where the Cedar Ridge all-stars were already warming up.

"Perfect," approved Rudy to Mike, who was jogging along beside him. "The soccer field goes right up to the trees. Here's the plan. We'll play for a little while to get the clones really excited. Then, when the time is right, I'm going to kick the ball into the woods. You go after it and keep on going. While they're looking for you, I'll slip away and we'll meet at the sign."

"But—" Mike began.

Rudy shrugged. "If you don't want to go, I'll look for that ball myself."

"I'll go," gulped Mike.

*   *   *

"It's five to nothing! Five to nothing!" howled Chip as Rudy manoeuvred his way up the field and kicked another goal.

Jack uttered a hoarse cry of joy and cast a triumphant look towards the Cedar Ridge counsellors, who were huddled on the sidelines trying to hide their dismay. Algonkian had always been an easy mark at soccer—and at everything else, for that matter. What was going on here? Who was this kid who had scored all their goals and handled a soccer ball as if it was glued to his feet?

On the field, Rudy stole the ball and began snaking his way through the Cedar Ridge players, relentlessly moving towards their goal. Out of the corner of his eye he saw Mike standing near the out-of-bounds line at the corner of the goal. Mike would never be in a better position than he was now. Rudy drew his leg back and kicked. The ball whizzed by the goal and sailed into the woods just beyond where Mike was positioned.

"I'll get it!" called Mike as he disappeared after the ball.

"He missed!" Chip exclaimed, astounded. "Miller *missed*!"

"It's about time too," growled the Cedar Ridge coach.

"But Miller doesn't miss. Ever." Chip turned to Jack. "Why would he miss?"

"Why wouldn't he?" said Jack impatiently. "He's human."

"Not Miller," Chip insisted. "He hits what he aims for."

"That's silly," said Jack. "You've hardly seen him play at all."

"I've seen enough," said Chip. "Enough to know he doesn't miss. *Why* did he miss?"

"I don't know," said Jack, beginning to pace. "Where's Webster with that ball?"

"Webster," repeated Chip. "Webster . . . *Miller!*"

Rudy was successfully mingling with the spectators on the sidelines, and edging himself ever closer to the trees.

"Hold that kid!" bellowed Chip, starting to run towards Rudy. "It's a trick!" he yelled over his shoulder at Jack. "A trick! You find Webster! I'll get Miller!"

Jack tore off into the woods where the ball and then Mike had disappeared.

Rudy tried to make for the woods, but the crowd of decidedly hostile Cedar Ridge campers crowded tightly around and kept him from making any progress. Finally he assumed a resigned look and raised his arms in surrender.

"Comrade," he said mildly as Chip came puffing up.

"Shut up, Miller! And get those hands down! Now, where's Webster?"

"Who?" asked Rudy innocently.

"Your accomplice! Webster!" yelled Chip.

"Sorry. Never heard of him" replied Rudy politely.

"Come on, Miller!" ordered Chip. "Tell me where to find Webster!"

"I'm afraid all I can give you is my name, rank and serial number," intoned Rudy.

"*Miller!*" roared Chip.

"Oh yes, you may torture me," said Rudy dramatically, noting that he had an astounded audience of Cedar Ridge campers and counsellors. "You may beat me. You may stick flaming bamboo under my fingernails. But I still won't give you any information."

"What's going on?" asked one of the Cedar Ridge counsellors. "What are you guys running over at Algonkian—a prison camp?"

"Yes," said Rudy pointedly.

Chip looked around, but Jack had still not returned. "Miller, if you don't start talking, I'll break your neck!"

"Dead, I am of no use to you," said Rudy calmly.

All at once the crowd was on Rudy's side.

"He's got a point there," laughed one of the counsellors.

"Leave him alone!"

"Pick on someone your own size!"

"Miller," begged Chip, "where's Webster? If he gets lost, something could happen to him!"

"You may hang me by my thumbs," replied Rudy, "or stretch me on the rack. You may stick my head in a blender, but I'll never tell."

By now, Cedar Ridge was hysterical with laughter.

Jack came loping out of the woods with the soccer ball but no Mike. "Where's Webster?"

"What do you mean where's Webster?" cried Chip. "I sent *you* after Webster!"

"At least I got the ball," said Jack. "As for Webster's whereabouts, let's squeeze it out of Miller."

"You may hold my head under water," Rudy continued, "or feed me to the alligators, but never will I break down."

"I wouldn't go to that Algonkian place!" said a very small camper fervently. "They torture you there!"

"And they've got alligators!"

"Hey," said one of the older boys to Rudy, "is it always like this at Algonkian?"

"No," said Rudy, poker-faced. "Sometimes it gets exciting."

"Where is he, where is he, *where is he?*" Chip was shouting. "Where's Webster?"

"Here," said a sheepish voice. The crowd parted and Mike, red-faced, walked up to face his counsellors.

"*Where were you?*" bellowed Chip.

"You only have to give your name, rank and serial number," Rudy reminded him.

"I couldn't find the ball?" suggested Mike hopefully.

"Can it!" snapped Chip. "I know where you were!"

"Then why did you ask?" said Rudy.

"Five more days work detail for the two of you!" yelled Chip.

"Hey, guys," put in Jack, "could we finish the game?"

"All right," said Chip sternly, "we're going to finish the game! Miller, Webster, no tricks, right?"

"Right," conceded Rudy and Mike.

Both teams took the field again.

* * *

Frank was waiting as the launch slipped into its place at the Algonkian Island dock.

"Well?" he asked Chip, who was the first one off. "How did we do?"

"Don't ask!" muttered Chip furiously, storming on by.

Frank turned to Jack. "You mean we lost?"

"No, we killed them," Jack replied. "Eleven to two. Miller scored ten goals."

"Oh," said Frank, bewildered. "Then, what in the world . . ."

* * *

". . . is eating you, Chip?" asked Frank at that evening's counsellors' meeting. "We won, didn't we? Our boy Miller clobbered them."

"Yes, and he also tried to run away again," stormed Chip. "Webster would have made it, too, if he hadn't got lost taking two steps without Miller. Miller hasn't reformed. He's worse than ever. He only agreed to play on the soccer team because it would get him to the mainland."

"But then why did he score all those goals?" asked Ralph, mystified. "Why did he bother to play so well if he only went there so he could run away?"

"As I see it," said Pierre, "that's Miller's character. He's honest, and he won't purposely play below his ability. I suppose the kid just doesn't like camp. It's not for everybody, you know. Maybe we should have told Mr. Warden a long time ago. But it's too late now. How do we let him know all this has been going on and we haven't told him?"

"I *tried* to tell him," Chip insisted, "the first time we

caught Miller and Webster lighting out in a boat. He didn't understand."

"He doesn't understand anything," said Frank. "We're just going to have to see this through."

"And we've got to keep tighter security on Miller," added Chip. "He can't be given an opportunity to go anywhere near the mainland. And he'll have to be under twenty-four hour surveillance, even on the island." He gestured helplessly. "Who knows what he could be doing right now?"

"What about the dance tomorrow at Silver Lake?" asked Leo Martin. "Everybody's going."

"No way!" snapped Chip. "I absolutely forbid it! Miller and Webster aren't going. Much as *I* want to go, I'll stay here with them."

"You can't do that," exclaimed Frank. "Everybody is supposed to go—all the campers and all of us."

"Not Miller and Webster! And not me, if that's what it takes to keep them here."

"All right," said Frank, "*you* explain it to Mr. Warden."

Chip swallowed hard. Then, "Well, if we really watch them, I suppose they can go."

There was a long silence. A strange look came over Chip's face, almost like a goofy grin, and he said, to no one in particular, "I like it better this way. I do. I could never get used to the idea of a nice peaceful Miller." He sighed. "This way at least I know where I stand."

* * *

All the boys were in bed, and Cabin 13 was dark. From the lower bunk in the far corner a foot rose and delivered a sharp kick to the mattress above it.

"Hey," whispered Mike, "what did you do that for?"

"That," said Rudy, "was for coming back when you were home free."

"I wasn't home free. I was lost," Mike defended himself.

"No one could get lost with such simple instructions," said Rudy. "Did you get to our meeting place?"

"Well—yeah."

"Then why did you come back?"

"Because you didn't come," said Mike. "So I went back to see what had happened, and I saw you were caught. So I gave myself up."

"Two stupids don't make a smart. You were free and you blew it. Now you'll have to spend another day here—maybe two."

"Then we're going again?" asked Mike in a small voice.

"Naturally," said Rudy. "Now get some sleep."

"I'm sorry, Rudy."

"Don't apologize to me." Rudy yawned. "Apologize to yourself."

12
Stop the music!

"A dance!" exclaimed Mike after breakfast the next day. He and Rudy were in arts and crafts, half-heart-edly sanding the wood for their tie racks. "Well, what do you know? The first decent activity they've come up with!"

"Calm down," said Rudy. "If they let us go, which I doubt after yesterday, then we won't be around there long enough to do any dancing. Escape, you know."

"Aw, Rudy, we'll never get away. They'll watch us like hawks. After our performance yesterday, we'll probably be bound and gagged and nailed to the wall of the dance hall!"

"I have it all figured out scientifically," said Rudy, his eyes gleaming. "Biologically, in fact. You see, Sil-ver Lake is a girls' camp. Therefore, they have girl clones. Once the dancing starts our clones, being of the male persuasion, will devote all their attention to the female clones. With the loud music and everything, we could probably stand at the door and wave and yell 'toodle-oo' and they'd never notice us. That's if we go at all. I have a feeling Chip won't let us."

"But that's not fair!" shouted Mike. "I want to go!"

Pierre ambled over. "What's all the yelling about?"

"World politics," said Rudy firmly.

"The dance, right?" grinned Pierre.

"They're not going to let us go!" yelled Mike. "It's not fair! I want to go!"

"Everyone's going," said Pierre. "Even you two."

"Oh," said Mike, embarrassed. "Oh, well, that's all right then."

"What about you, Miller?" asked Pierre. "Don't you want to go?"

Rudy shrugged indifferently. "Well, we're going to be eating there, and the food just has to be better than here," he said. "But I don't dance."

Pierre laughed out loud. "The last thing you didn't do was play soccer, and you managed ten goals!"

"I don't dance," repeated Rudy stubbornly.

"Sure," said Pierre sarcastically. "Keep sanding those tie racks." He walked away.

Mike looked at Rudy. "*Do* you dance?"

"Only at gunpoint."

"No, I mean *can* you dance?"

"So I'm told," said Rudy.

If Mike had not known better, he would have been sure he saw a distinct flush on Rudy's cheeks.

* * *

"I just hope I'm doing the right thing," said Chip at a mid-afternoon impromptu counsellors' meeting. "I mean, I know Miller's going to try to run away. I know it. You know it, Frank—we all know it. Why on earth are we taking him to the mainland?"

"Maybe the girls will keep him there," suggested Frank hopefully.

"He says he doesn't dance," offered Pierre, "if that's any comfort."

"He's probably the world's greatest dancer," muttered Ralph.

"Well," said Pierre, "take this for what it's worth: Webster wants to dance. If Webster doesn't try to run away, maybe Miller won't."

There were murmurs of agreement.

"But we can't count on that," said Chip anxiously. "They have to be watched every second!"

"Don't worry," said Frank. "It'll be all right."

"I wish I could believe that," moaned Chip.

* * *

"You," accused Rudy, "have been combing your hair for fifteen minutes."

Mike grinned. "I've got to look good," he argued.

"Why is Chip letting the nut go?" complained Harold Greene, washing his face. "He'll wreck the whole dance!"

"Keep scrubbing your face, Harold," said Rudy genially, "and maybe some of the twit will rub off."

"Shut up!" snapped Harold. "Hey, what's that awful smell?"

"That's Joey's aftershave," said Adam, wrinkling his nose.

"But he doesn't shave!"

Adam shrugged. "That doesn't matter to him."

"How long until it's our turn for the launch?" asked Mike. "Maybe I've got time to take another shower."

"You're as clean as it's possible to be without being boiled," said Rudy. "Besides, we've only got five minutes. Come on."

* * *

At five o'clock that afternoon, the boys of Algonkian Island, scrubbed and shining, marched happily into the dining room of Camp Silver Lake. Mike Webster was the first to arouse the girls' curiosity, as he was being personally escorted to his seat by Ralph Deacon and Jack Tyler. But their attention was almost immediately diverted by the arrival of six tall counsellors who stepped inside and arranged themselves on either side of the door in military fashion. Then in marched Rudy Miller, sandwiched between Chip and Frank, each one with a hand on his shoulder. The remainder of the Algonkian counsellors brought up the rear. Chip and Frank led Rudy to a vacant seat beside Mike and sat him down.

Rudy looked around the table of boys and girls. "Maximum security," he explained.

Mike laughed. "If my parents had seen me escorted here under guard . . . "

"My parents would have thought it was par for the course," commented Rudy dryly.

"All right," said Chip, smiling broadly. "I'm Chip."

"And I'm Jane," replied a counsellor from Silver Lake.

"And I'm Tarzan," murmured Rudy.

Mike snickered.

"Quit that, Webster!" snapped Chip. "Now, one by one, let's hear your names."

"Joey."

"Adam."

"Mary."

"Grace."

"Mike."

"Zeke."

"*Miller!*" yelled Chip. "Don't fool around!"

"Oh, all right. Rudy."

Grace turned to Mary. "I think he's cute." She giggled.

"Okay," said Jane when they had finished, "let's see who remembers all the names. How about you, Rudy?"

Rudy blinked twice and began to recite with computer accuracy: "Joey, Adam, Mary, Grace, Mike, myself, Barbara, Harold Greene, Brian, Jane..." He paused and stared at Chip in perplexity. "What was your name again?"

"Chip! *Chip!*"

"So much for bird calls," said Rudy. "What's your name?"

"Oh, stop it, Miller!" Chip turned to petite, blue-eyed Jane. "Okay, how do we go about getting some food into this lot?"

"Intravenously?" suggested Rudy.

Everyone laughed except Chip, who sighed deeply. "Miller..." he warned under his breath.

The kitchen staff began to arrive with huge platters of hot dogs, hamburgers and french fries. Soon everyone was happily eating.

"Can it be?" said Rudy faintly. "Yes, it is—food. Real food."

All the girls laughed, including Jane.

"Don't they have real food at Algonkian?" asked Barbara.

"Only a little swill now and then," said Rudy, reaching for a hot dog. "Served in a trough, of course."

"Come on, Miller," said Chip a little angrily. "These

people will think Algonkian's a terrible place."

"The public has a right to know," said Rudy solemnly.

Everyone laughed, even Chip. although he was obviously forcing himself to do so.

"So," began Jane amiably, looking around the table, "what do you fellows do for excitement at Algonkian?"

"Oh, well," said Adam, "we play a lot of sports— you know, baseball, soccer and all that stuff."

"And we swim," added Harold. "That's excluding Miller and Webster, of course. They sit around all day and play chess."

"Eat!" commanded Chip. He felt his dinner sticking in his throat. Things were not going to be comfortable until Miller and Webster were back on Algonkian Island. This was going to be a long evening.

* * *

Escorted by Chip and Frank, Rudy Miller entered the recreation hall and immediately walked over and seated himself on a corner bench. The hall began to fill up, and before long the lights were low and the music was pounding its heavy, floor-shaking beat.

Mike sidled up to Rudy. "You're not going to sit here all night, are you?"

Rudy glanced casually at Chip, who was dancing with Jane but keeping an eye on the bench. Then, deciding that there was no possible way Chip or anyone else could overhear him, he replied, "No, I'm not going to sit here all night. You see that door over there? Somehow, in the next hour or so, I'm going to be out of it and gone. Are you coming?"

"Aw, Rudy," whined Mike, "I like it here!"

"Yes, I know," said Rudy patiently, "but you have to remember that after *here*, you go back *there*. The cell door closes and you're back to square one."

"Yeah," argued Mike, "but—"

"It's up to you." Rudy shrugged.

"I'll go," said Mike quickly. "What do I have to do?"

"I haven't thought of that yet," said Rudy. "Just watch me. I'll signal you."

A group of girls, led by Barbara, Mary and Grace, arrived on the scene and seated themselves around Rudy.

"Hi, Rudy," said Barbara. "We're curious about you."

"In what way?" asked Rudy absently, raising a disinterested eyebrow as he checked out the opportunities for escape.

The blonde girl shrugged. "You're different. For instance, your counsellors treat you like a prisoner. How come?"

"I *am* a prisoner," said Rudy. "We all are, only some of us notice it more than others."

"Aren't you enjoying yourself?" asked Grace.

"Hardly," said Rudy blandly.

"That's because you're not dancing!" exclaimed Mary. "Come on, girls! Let's get him out on the floor!"

Mike watched open-mouthed as the group, which had now grown to eight girls, dragged Rudy bodily out onto the dance floor.

"I don't dance," Rudy was saying, his calm unruffled.

"Dancing is easy," insisted Mary, swaying to the

beat of the music. "This is all there is to it." The rest of the girls began to dance as though demonstrating.

The idea suddenly occurred to Rudy that only by dancing was he going to get off the bench and out from under Chip's scrutiny. He began to move in time to the music with a perfect technique and agility that left everyone gasping. His arms and legs became a controlled blur, and his slim athletic body gyrated to the beat of the music as if he had been born and raised in its rhythm.

"I worried about him," Mike muttered darkly to himself. "Now he's got eight partners and I've got none!"

"You were holding out on us," laughed Mary. "You're an expert. Stick with me and we'll knock 'em dead!"

"I don't dance," insisted Rudy. He executed a perfect double spin without missing a beat.

Pierre walked over and leaned against the wall next to Mike. "Our friend Miller is full of surprises," he commented.

Mike grinned. "You'd be surprised."

Pierre laughed. "If he's not careful, somebody might think he's enjoying himself."

"Ha!" said Mike. The thought of Rudy Miller enjoying anything that had to do with camp was absurd. "Rudy hasn't changed expression since the day he arrived at Algonkian."

"I stand corrected," said Pierre. "Look at him now—dancing up a storm with seven or eight girls and looking as bored as if he were reading the telephone book. How do you figure him?"

"I don't," said Mike. "And we're still friends. I have a feeling that's why."

"Hey!" came a shout from across the room. Chip had glanced towards the bench and found it empty. "Where's Miller?"

"Take it easy," soothed Jane, his dancing partner. "There's your Miller right over there, dancing with my entire group—and can he ever dance!"

Chip stared in amazement and then broke into a joyous laugh. "Well, what do you know? We finally found Miller's weakness—women! Miller has a weakness for women!"

"I'd say the women have a weakness for Miller," laughed Jane.

"But he's having fun," insisted Chip. "Miller doesn't have fun. At least not until now. This is fantastic!"

"I'm glad," said Jane sarcastically. "Now maybe you'll relax and have a little fun yourself."

Rudy was still going strong, taking on new partners as the original eight began to drop out, exhausted. Mike had managed to secure a tall, tanned girl named Laura, and they were dancing as close to Rudy as they dared without risking physical harm. His flailing arms and legs presented a clear and present danger.

"I hope I don't look too ridiculous," came Rudy's bored voice out of the tornado.

"You look great," Laura assured him. "Who taught you to dance?"

"A mixmaster," replied Rudy. "Say, Mike, I'm planning to invent a new dance. It's called The Exit. Are you with me?"

Mike swallowed hard. "Yeah."

"It sounds super," raved Laura. "Will you teach it to me?"

"Uh—" began Mike.

"Sure," said Rudy. "First we start to dance towards that door."

"Oh," said Laura. "That kind of exit. Where are you going?"

"Home, never to be seen again in these parts. Come on, Mike, we're starting now." He turned to his several partners, who had all heard bits and pieces of the conversation through the din of the music. "Thank you very much for the dance. It's been nifty."

Before the girls' astonished eyes, Rudy and Mike danced off, weaving in and out across the packed dance floor towards the door. Rudy opened the door and shoved Mike outside. Then, executing a devastating triple spin, he was gone as though in a puff of smoke.

*　*　*

"Hi, Miller." Pierre was sitting in a comfortable lawn chair facing the recreation hall exit. "I kind of figured you'd be along soon." One hand rested easily on the arm of the chair. With the other hand he held Mike Webster tightly by the belt.

A smile almost showed itself on Rudy's passive face, and his eyes gleamed in the darkness. "Curses," he said mildly, "foiled again."

Pierre turned to Mike. "You said I'd be surprised. I wasn't. Well, now—do you consider yourselves officially caught, or the minute I let go of Webster do you both take off?"

"Try me," said Rudy softly.

Pierre laughed into the darkness. "I think I will." He released Mike, reached behind the chair and produced two more folding chairs. "Sit down," he invited. "We're going to talk about all this."

The two boys sat down. Rudy glanced at Mike. "Remember—name, rank and serial number."

Mike giggled nervously.

"Come on, Miller," said Pierre. "You're not talking to Chip now. If you're trying to drive *me* crazy, you'll have to do a little better than that."

Rudy raised both eyebrows and looked mildly interested.

"As you can see," began Pierre, "I've thought of everything. And I've even figured you out, Miller. You—"

From inside the recreation hall came three sharp whistle blasts, followed by Chip's half-demented voice screaming, "Stop! Stop the music! Miller's gone! Miller's g-o-o-o-ne!"

The heavy beat of the music stopped abruptly, to be replaced by a louder, horrifying sound. Pandemonium broke loose in the dance hall. There were shouts and the sound of running feet. The door burst open and out stampeded all the Algonkian counsellors, Chip in the lead.

"Chip! Frank! Stop!" cried Pierre. "*Wait—*"

Nobody looked at him sitting there with the two boys.

Behind the counsellors swarmed all the Algonkian boys, laughing, shouting and hooting in the night.The Silver Lake girls and their counsellors came last, happy and laughing in spite of their confusion.

"What's going on?"

"It's got to be that Rudy Miller."

"You mean the weird guy?"

"He's the cutest guy I ever danced with!"

"Let's go find him!"

"Maybe if we find him we can keep him! They sure don't want him!"

"Hey," announced Barbara triumphantly, "here he is—sitting right here!"

"Hi, Rudy," said Mary. "Come on back inside. We haven't finished our dance."

"I don't dance," said Rudy quietly.

"Ohhhh!" moaned Pierre. "That Chip! How are we going to round everybody up?"

"Obviously you *didn't* think of everything," said Rudy righteously. "But Mike and I can go along and help you look for everybody. Right, Mike?"

"Right," squeaked Mike.

"No way, Miller. If I could trust you two, I'd be able to go find them myself."

"Why don't you leave them with us?" suggested Jane.

Pierre looked at her, a tiny figure surrounded by ten or eleven Silver Lake girls. Everyone else was gone on the search. Then it occurred to him that it would be justice to leave Miller here. They would make him dance, something Miller seemed to hold on a par with baseball and soccer.

"That's a good idea. Thanks," said Pierre, turning to go.

The gleam in Rudy's eye faded abruptly. "Take us with you," he said, rather more quickly than was usual for him.

"No," laughed Pierre. "I wouldn't want to spoil

your fun. You go in there and dance. And in case Chip forgets to mention it, that's five more days work detail for each of you." He ran off into the darkness.

Jane and the girls ushered Rudy and Mike inside the recreation hall.

"Come on, Rudy," said Jane enthusiastically. "Teach me how to dance the way you do."

"Do I have an alternative?" asked Rudy.

"Yes," said Jane with an endearing smile. "Push-ups."

Rudy nodded. "Would somebody please put on a record?"

* * *

The counsellors' meeting back on Algonkian Island late that night was a spirited affair. With the exception of Pierre, all the counsellors were in a state of rage brought on by a two hour intensive wild-goose chase.

"Tomorrow," roared Chip, "Miller dies! I don't care about my job! He dies!"

Pierre laughed in his face. "Don't be ridiculous. Miller didn't throw you in the lake. You fell in — you and Frank and Ralph and Jack."

"That's enough out of you," snapped Frank. "Why didn't you tell us you were right outside the rec hall with Miller and Webster?"

"A millimetre to the left," retorted Pierre, "and you would have tripped over us. Why didn't you look?"

"It was dark," lamented Ralph. "And nobody told me there was a lake!"

"That's why they call the place Silver Lake," Pierre explained patiently. "Because there's this lake — a silver one."

"Now you're sounding like Miller," warned Chip. "Don't you dare sound like Miller or tomorrow you die too!" He brought his fist down to pound the table, but it landed in the pot of hot soup that had been prepared for the four wet counsellors. "*Ow!*"

"Do you expect me to eat that now?" growled Frank.

Pierre was hysterical with laughter.

"I'd like to know what's so funny, Mr. Arts and Crafts!" demanded George Harper of Cabin 1. "I chased a squirrel up a tree because I thought it was Miller. I fell and almost killed myself!"

"And wait till Dave gets back tomorrow," said Jack. "When he phoned he didn't sound too pleased that we forgot him there. He was sprayed by a skunk, you know, and that's no picnic! He's got no change of clothes, and they won't even let him into their wash station to clean up!"

"No more," moaned Pierre, rolling in his chair. "I don't want to hear any more! Please!"

"What about me?" cried Jim Goldfarb of Cabin 18. "I'm lucky to be alive! I ran into a bear in those woods! A real bear! If I hadn't kicked at it and scared it away—"

"*You!* Was that you?" shouted big Leo Martin. "That was *me* you kicked! Me! I'm not a bear!"

"Then why did you reach for me?" cried Jim.

"I thought you were Miller!"

"I'm going to write a book about this!" raved Pierre. "It'll be a best-seller!" Tears rolled down his cheeks.

"And as if I hadn't been through enough," finished Chip as though no one else had spoken, "I get back to the rec hall soaking wet and looking like an idiot and what do I find? Miller, dancing with Jane—*my* date! It's too much! I tell you, it's the end!"

The meeting lapsed into angry silence. Chip clenched his fists, Ralph sneezed violently, Jim Goldfarb and Leo Martin scowled at one another, and Jack lapped sulkily at a bowl of soup. Pierre wore a grin that stretched from ear to ear.

Finally Frank spoke. "If I wasn't so filled with anger, hatred and self-pity, I swear I'd be laughing my head off!"

Leo Martin's scowl bloomed into a toothy smile. "Jim thought I was a bear!"

"I kicked him!" guffawed Jim.

"And all for nothing," said Jack quietly. "Miller didn't even get away. How about that?" He broke into gales of laughter.

"Dave!" snickered Frank. "We forgot Dave!"

"He's always complaining he never gets off the island," added Pierre hysterically. "When he gets back, he'll never leave again!"

The merriment was contagious, and soon all the counsellors, with the exception of Chip, were roaring with laughter.

"What's all this stupid laughing?" Chip shouted. "What's so funny?"

"Us!" howled Frank breathlessly. "We almost killed ourselves! Silver Lake thinks we're a bunch of crazy savages! And it was all for *nothing!*"

An odd look came over Chip's face. Ridiculous. So ridiculous. Everything had gone wrong. Everything. Four guys in the lake. Jim kicking Leo. George up a tree. Dave, sprayed and stranded. And Miller, the cause of it all and yet not really responsible, dancing his way through the whole insane business. Miller was so—so funny!

He threw his head back and began to laugh, not just at the events of the evening, but at everything. That Miller!

* * *

The beaver lay at peace on a bed of soft pine needles and gazed upon his masterpiece. At last, the dam was completed. And a beautiful dam it was, constructed with all his skill. He sensed rain in the air, but it would still be a day or two before it came. Then his dam would be tested.

13
Mist off the lake

Before breakfast the next morning Chip assembled the occupants of Cabin 13 in front of the building.

"Boy, oh boy," commented Mike nervously to Rudy, "we're really going to get it! I've never seen the clones so mad as last night coming home on that bus!"

"I wonder if they've found out they forgot Dave," said Rudy mildly.

"You mean they left him at Silver Lake?" cried Mike. "And you knew? And you didn't tell anyone?"

Rudy shrugged, his eyes gleaming. "Chip told me to shut up, so I did."

"Well, you guys," said Chip, walking up and down in front of the boys like a drill sergeant, "tomorrow is visiting day."

"Already?" said Rudy in mock surprise.

"Yep," said Chip philosophically. "Time sure flies when you're having fun."

There was a half-insane titter from Mike.

"Can it, Webster!" snapped Chip. "Okay, seriously, guys—your parents are coming tomorrow and the camp has to look terrific, right?"

"Wrong," said Rudy firmly. "If this is a plea for

unpaid labour, I want you to know I don't clean."

A scowl formed on Chip's face, but with effort he turned it into a big smile. "Oh, yes you do, Miller. You do lots of things. You'd be amazed at what you do."

"In other words," said Rudy, "you're planning to use force to make me help tidy up the camp."

"Right," grinned Chip. "Okay guys, visiting day means that camp is half over. Let's make the second half even better than the first."

"It can hardly miss," deadpanned Rudy.

"And," added Chip meaningfully, "let's have some of us trying to improve our behaviour, shall we?"

"I think he means us," Rudy stage-whispered to Mike.

Mike snickered loudly.

"Okay," said Chip. "There's a lot of work to be done around the place. Let's have some volunteers."

Rudy's hand shot into the air. "Mike and I volunteer to tidy up the boating dock."

Chip laughed out loud. "No chance, Miller. You and Webster are going to work where I can watch you."

"There's no trust in this place," lamented Rudy.

"No, not since you came along," said Chip. "come on, now, where are my volunteers?"

Rudy's hand shot up again. "Mike and I volunteer to go and test the main motor launch," he offered. "We wouldn't want our parents to have a rough ride or to sink or anything."

"No, thank you, Miller," grinned Chip. "Now look, you guys, you're standing here waiting for breakfast. I

162

want some volunteers or"—he glanced at Rudy—"you don't eat."

Rudy nodded approvingly.

"I'll sweep out the bunk," offered Adam.

"I'll pick up litter in the compound," said Joey.

"I'll help clean the mess hall."

"I can help Joey with the litter."

"I'll wash the mess hall windows."

"I'll supervise the entire operation," offered Rudy.

"Come on, Miller," said Chip. "You and Webster are going to scrub our floor."

"I don't do floors, windows or anything else," said Rudy plaintively.

"You do now," said Chip. "Come on, you guys. Let's go to breakfast."

* * *

"Look at that!" boasted Chip as several of his counsellor friends filed through Cabin 13. "There's the soccer champion of the whole world, there's the heaviest hitter in baseball, there's the greatest chess master in history, there's the dancing darling of Silver Lake, there's the king of the disappearing act himself! He and his faithful side-kick are scrubbing the floor!"

On his hands and knees on the floor, Rudy looked up at his audience with a paralysingly cold glare. Then he resumed his work. Mike just kept on scrubbing, tight-lipped and red-faced.

"Yes," said Chip, "I've finally found Miller's weakness. He's afraid of being beaten to death. I just told him about the days when I was my old high school's boxing champion."

Pierre laughed. "He could probably knock your head off."

"It does your heart good to see him on his knees," sighed Ralph.

"What are you going to do now, Miller?" taunted Frank. "Climb in that bucket and sail away?"

Rudy stood up and folded his arms. "Gentlemen, Mike and I don't like the working conditions here. We"—he pulled Mike to his feet—"are on strike."

"Yeah," squeaked Mike.

Pierre started to laugh. "You've got a big mouth, Frank, and a big foot to fit in it. You too, Chip."

"Miller—" said Chip warningly.

"We're on strike," Rudy repeated. "We've got to get over to arts and crafts to paint some signs so we can picket."

"Arts and crafts is all cleaned up and closed for tomorrow," said Pierre, "but I'd be happy to open it up for you."

"Hey, whose side are you on?" snapped Chip.

"That's quite obvious," said Pierre. "Now—this is how you handle a situation like this. Miller, Webster, be good joes and finish the floor."

"Gee, we'd like to," said Rudy, "but it's against union regulations."

"I'll give him union regulations!" hollered Chip, shaking a big fist.

"Tell you what I'll do," said Pierre. "We're working under a tight deadline here, so I'll double your salaries."

"Oh, well," said Rudy, "in that case the strike is settled." He and Mike dropped down to their hands and knees and continued scrubbing.

Chip was dumbfounded. "Boy, is Miller ever stupid!" he whispered. "He doesn't get a salary!"

Pierre shook his head resignedly. "The problem isn't Miller."

*　*　*

Visiting day dawned dark and threatening. The air was still and muggy, and clouds hung low over the lake.

Frank knocked on the camp office door.

"Come in," said Mr. Warden.

"Uh—sir," began the head counsellor, "I hate to say this, but it looks like rain. I guess we'd better cancel the outdoor buffet and serve lunch in the mess hall."

"Nonsense, my boy," said Arthur Warden jovially. "I've seen a hundred mornings like this at Algonkian. Since the days of my grandfather, it hasn't rained once for an Algonkian parents' day. It's just the mist off the lake. It'll clear up."

"But sir—" protested Frank, who had heard a rumble of thunder in the distance.

"Now, now, do as I say," reproached Mr. Warden. "Set up for the buffet."

"Yes, sir," murmured Frank. Shaking his head, he left the office. "It's still on," he told his waiting crew.

"Is he nuts?" exploded Chip. "We're going to drown those parents!"

"It isn't going to rain," insisted Frank sarcastically. "Elias wouldn't stand for it."

"Oh, no," lamented Ralph Deacon. "In the middle of a thunderstorm we're going to have a picnic. And all because it's not allowed to rain on visiting day. Elias's law."

*　*　*

"Liberation day," declared Rudy, animated as usual by the thought of leaving Algonkian Island. He was stuffing his things into his duffle bag. "I hope my folks are the first to arrive. That way we can be the first to leave."

"Should I be packing too?" asked Mike.

"Everyone who is going home today should be packing," said Rudy.

Mike strummed on his guitar, which had just been returned to him that morning. "Good as new," he commented. "It was nice of them to get it fixed, wasn't it, Rudy?"

"They're all heart," said Rudy sarcastically. "Remember, if *you* had smashed up the cabin you'd have had to fix your own guitar."

Mike took out his suitcase and began neatly folding T-shirts.

Adam Willis walked in and stared at Rudy and Mike in surprise. "Hey, why are you packing? You guys haven't been kicked out, have you?"

"No such luck," said Rudy.

Adam laughed.

"We're hoping our parents will take us home," explained Mike.

Adam looked genuinely sorry. "Gee, that's too bad."

"No, it isn't," said Rudy. "It's good. Very good."

Adam laughed again. "Well, I'll say this for you, Miller. You're a terrible camper, but you're the best camp director we ever had."

Rudy stopped his packing and looked at the boy intently for a moment. "Even better than old Elias?"

"Heck," said Adam, grinning, "that was before my

time." He sobered. "You know, it's going to be pretty dull here without you guys."

Rudy pointed to the suitcase under Adam's bed. "Pack," he suggested.

"Oh, not me. I kind of like it here."

Rudy shook his head. "And you seem so sensible."

"Another thing about your leaving," Adam said, playing his last trump card, "is that it'll make Harold Greene so happy."

Rudy froze. "It almost makes me want to stay. Almost." He rummaged in his suitcase and came out with a marking pen and a piece of paper. Then, in a flowing script which showed that he was as skilled at calligraphy as he was at baseball, he wrote:

Betwixt these sheets sleepeth ye biggest twit in Ontario.

Eyeing it with evident though unsmiling pleasure, he affixed it with a bandaid to Harold Greene's pillow.

* * *

The launch bringing the first group of parents arrived shortly before eleven. By noon all the parents, brothers and sisters were on the island enjoying a reunion with the campers.

Eight-year-old Jeffrey Miller was looking distastefully around the compound. "What a stupid place!" he announced loudly. "Mom, why did you send Rudy to such a stupid place?"

Chip, who had been chatting with Rudy's father, turned abruptly and stared at Jeffrey, marvelling at his resemblance to Rudy, not only in looks but in attitude.

"I taught him everything he knows," said Rudy proudly.

"I noticed," muttered Chip, moving off.

"Hey, Rudy," piped Jeffrey, "How come all the counsellors look alike?"

"They're cloned," explained Rudy. He pointed at Frank. "From him."

A smiling Mike Webster walked over with his mother, father and younger sister in tow. "Mom, Dad, Vicky—I want you to meet my friend Rudy Miller."

Rudy solemnly shook hands all around and introduced his own parents and Jeffrey.

Vicky turned large worshipful eyes on Rudy. "Is it really true that you're the best baseball player in the world?"

Rudy glared at Mike. "What kind of letters have you been writing?"

Mike shrugged. "I couldn't write about what a wonderful time I was having, so I wrote all about you."

"Speaking of letters," remarked Rudy's mother, "you wrote us an identical letter every time."

"Not exactly," said Rudy calmly. "The number of days until visiting day varied with each one."

Mike leaned over to Rudy. "Have you asked them to take you home yet?" he whispered.

"Not yet," said Rudy. "I'm waiting until after lunch. Once they've tasted the food here they'll have a better understanding of why I want to leave."

"Look," announced Jeffrey loudly, "here come some more of those clone guys!"

In a group, Frank, Ralph, Jack, Leo, Pierre and Dave walked over and introduced themselves to Rudy's parents.

"I sure wanted to meet you folks," said Ralph.

"Me too!" echoed the others fervently.

Susan Miller turned to her husband. "The other parents don't seem to be getting this kind of attention, dear. I'm afraid Rudy has been at it again."

"Has he been behaving himself?" Mr. Miller asked Frank.

"Oh, we wouldn't know anything about that," said Frank quickly. "You'll have to ask Chip, his bunk counsellor."

"I was speaking to this Chip," said Mr. Miller. "But every time I asked him about Rudy he changed the subject."

"Oh, Rudy!" exclaimed his mother in exasperation.

From the direction of Cabin 13, Chip approached, his face beet-red, a synthetic smile showing all his teeth. "Excuse me, please. I'd like to have a private word with Miller and Webster."

Rudy and Mike followed him to a secluded area near the cabins. From his pocket Chip produced the sign from Harold Greene's bed.

"Miller, did you do this?"

"Yes," said Rudy briskly. "Elegant, isn't it?"

"It's downright nasty!" said Chip angrily. "His parents almost saw it!"

"Well, it should come as no great shock to them," said Rudy reasonably. "They know he's a twit. They're his parents, after all."

"*Miller!*"

"He's yelling, Mom!" came Jeffrey Miller's high-pitched voice. "The clone is yelling at Rudy!"

"*Two* of you!" exclaimed Chip. "Two Millers!" He laughed and walked away, shaking his head.

"Oh, dear," said Mike's mother, "it looks as though our Michael and your boy have been in some kind of mischief."

"Oh, I wouldn't worry," said Susan Miller. "I'm sure that if it were anything serious we'd have been notified."

"What did they do wrong, Mom?" asked Vicky.

"I'm sure it's nothing too bad, dear," said Mrs. Webster, smiling. "The boys are just high-spirited because they're having such a good time at camp."

"I wonder . . . " said Mrs. Miller thoughtfully, gazing at her sober-faced older son.

* * *

"The Millers look like ordinary people—nice people!" exclaimed Ralph Deacon.

"But those kids," put in Chip. "Did you see the younger one? He's almost as bad as Miller!"

"Shhh!" said Frank sharply. "Mr. Warden's about to speak."

Mr. Warden rose and approached the microphone. "Greetings, campers and visitors. My name is Arthur Warden, and I'm the camp director. This is Camp Algonkian Island. It was founded thirty-one years ago by my grandfather, Elias Warden."

"Dad, why are his legs like that?" asked Jeffrey Miller loudly.

"Shh, Jeff!"

"Somewhere in that crowd," whispered Chip to Frank, "Webster is laughing his head off. Somehow he always gets a charge out of Mr. Warden's speeches."

Frank grimaced. "I know these speeches by heart

and they're no laughing matter. Our boss could put a stone to sleep."

"This is the thirty-first annual Parents' Visiting Day," the camp director went on. "I invite all of you to join me in our traditional outdoor buffet luncheon. I look forward to chatting with as many of you as possible. Please enjoy yourselves."

Everyone turned to the buffet, which consisted of three long tables set up in the compound near the mess hall. Lunch was an appetizing display of sandwiches and salads. Cake, ice cream and drinks were being served at a smaller fourth table.

"*Yecch!*" exclaimed Jeffrey Miller, chewing gingerly at an egg sandwich. "Boy, this food is terrible! Rudy, do they make you eat this every day?"

Rudy nodded. "Yes, they do. But usually it's much worse. The cook makes a beef stew you could build a mud hut with."

"You! Miller! Shut up!" The cook stood, arms akimbo, glaring at Rudy and his brother.

"Gee, Rudy, everybody knows you," said Jeffrey proudly.

Mr. and Mrs. Miller walked up to where Mr. Warden, Frank at his side, was receiving some of the parents.

"I'm Edward Miller and this is my wife, Susan. We're Rudy's parents." They waited expectantly.

"How do you do?" said Mr. Warden blandly.

"We wrote you a letter about Rudy," said Mrs. Miller anxiously, "about how difficult he can be, and how he didn't want to go to camp."

Frank turned pale. "There was a letter?" he blurted.

Mr. Warden smiled serenely. "Oh, yes, I remember. His school guidance counsellor recommended camp. Overanxious parents," he chided gently. "Your son has been just fine here, as I knew he would be. He fit right in, isn't that right, Frank?"

Frank coughed violently to cover his consternation and swallowed hard. "Yes—Miller—amazing kid." He turned disbelieving eyes on his employer. "You received a *letter* about Rudy Miller?" He cleared his throat carefully. "You—didn't mention anything."

Mr. Warden smiled wisely. "Since the days of my grandfather, Elias Warden, boys haven't changed," he said. "They're all born to go to camp."

"Well, I'm glad everything worked out," said Mrs. Miller dubiously. "It was very nice meeting you." Rudy's parents walked away, eyeing Frank thoughtfully.

He knew, thought Frank in a cold fury, seeking out a nearby bench and sitting down heavily. I don't believe it. There was a warning about Miller and he didn't tell anybody! When Chip and the guys hear about this they'll throw Warden in the lake!

Frank took a deep breath and most of the colour returned to his face. Why put the guys through that? he thought. Especially Chip, who had been driven to desperation by Miller's exploits. This was one revelation he'd keep to himself.

His mouth full of potato salad, Chip walked over to where Frank was sitting. "Well, the boss was right," he mumbled. "It didn't rain on his buffet."

As if timed by some evil force of nature, the sky was rent by a jagged fork of lightning, followed almost immediately by a deafening clap of thunder. Without any further warning, the heavens opened and the rain came in a blinding downpour.

"This way, folks!" shouted Frank, now fully recovered from his shock and ready to take charge. He had been prepared for just such an emergency. "Into the mess hall!"

People began scurrying towards the shelter of the building, the Algonkian staff and some of the campers carrying the various plates of food. Chip grabbed the huge platter of potato salad and began to run across the already muddy ground towards the mess hall. Rudy, Mike and Jeffrey watched as, with a strangled cry, Chip slipped on the wet grass, then tripped over the doorstep and fell full-length into the mess hall, his face buried in the potato salad. The screen door blew shut, closing on Chip's mid-section. He lay there, his head in the salad, his legs in the rain.

Frank and Dave came running to the door and hauled Chip inside. The awkard silence that followed was broken by a peal of laughter from Jeffrey Miller. This set Mike off, and soon the whole mess hall— campers, counsellors and parents alike—was rollicking with mirth.

Sticky and humiliated, Chip ventured out into the raging storm to go to the wash station to clean up.

"I may have been wrong about this camp!" piped up Jeffrey enthusiastically. "This is fun!"

Rudy stared at Jeffrey and then at Mike. Mike looked back intently.

* * *

"Man, this is the worst storm I've ever seen!" exclaimed Chip. "It's been coming down like this for over an hour!"

"I've never seen it rain so hard," moaned Frank. "What are we going to do with the parents for the rest of the afternoon? Everyone's getting restless."

"We sure can't have the soccer game," agreed Chip, gazing out the screen door of the mess hall where all were still trapped by the downpour. "The field's flooded. *Hey*, the field's *flooded!*"

There was a stampede of counsellors to the door.

"The field should be wet, but it shouldn't be flooded like that!" exclaimed Jack.

"Look at the water!" gasped Chip.

"There must be fifteen or twenty centimetres of it!" cried Frank. "Mr. Warden! Where's Mr. Warden?"

"In his cottage," said Pierre. "He took off when the rain started. I suppose I'd better go and get him. Elias would have wanted the captain to go down with the camp." He dashed off through the mud and the rain towards the camp director's cottage.

"What's going on?" called one of the parents.

"Nothing to worry about," smiled Frank reassuringly. "Everything is under control."

"Under control?" howled Chip. "Under control? It's a flood!"

There was a murmur throughout the mess hall as people began to feel uneasy.

"Unless I miss my guess," said Ralph in a low voice, "that water is spreading in this direction."

Rudy and Mike pushed their way to the door. "What's going on?" asked Rudy mildly.

"Get out of here, Miller!" barked Chip. "We've got enough trouble. We don't need you!"

The two boys and their counsellors stood in open-mouthed amazement as the water came on in a steady, shallow flow. It engulfed the mess hall and continued towards the cabins and other buildings, surrounding them and flowing on towards the lake.

"It's coming in!" shouted Chip.

The water had begun to seep in through the door and from under the floor boards. Soon everyone was up to the ankles in water, and still more was seeping in.

"Wow," exclaimed Mike in the general excitement, "a disaster! A natural disaster! Rudy, our natural disaster!"

Rudy's studied poker face began to disintegrate. His eyes gleamed, then danced. A smile cracked the veneer of his normally expressionless face. It grew until it extended from ear to ear. Rudy Miller laughed. He put his head in his hands and began to laugh uncontrollably, splashing his way over to the wall for support.

Mike was thunderstruck. He had never even seen Rudy smile, let alone laugh.

"Cut it out, Webster!" snapped Chip. "It isn't funny!"

"It's not me!" Mike protested, almost speechless. "It's—him!" He pointed at Rudy who was still doubled over with mirth, tears now streaming down his cheeks.

Chip stared in amazement. "Miller. *Miller*!"

Pierre staggered in the door, completely drenched.

"Did you get him?" asked Frank anxiously. "Where's Mr. Warden?"

"Trapped!" gasped Pierre. "His cottage is in a valley and the water is up over the windows! He waved at me from the attic. He's okay."

"But we're not okay!" roared Frank. "What are we going to do?"

"There must be a blockage in the creek," suggested Pierre. "If a few of us can get in there and unblock it, the water will eventually either evaporate or drain into the lake, once it stops raining. Come on. I need eight or ten guys."

"Mike and I will go," choked Rudy.

"Just counsellors," ordered Frank. "Chip, Chip!"

"Miller was laughing," said Chip abstractedly.

"He would be," said Frank. "I always knew it would take a disaster to get Miller to crack a smile. Now, come on. We've got to go and unblock the creek."

A dozen counsellors sloshed their way out the door and headed towards the woods.

"Boy, Ma," exclaimed Jeffrey Miller loudly, "terrific stuff happens here! Can I go to camp here next year?"

* * *

"Ah," said Rudy Miller, his poker face reassumed, "things are looking up for the desperate flood victims. The sun is shining and Alcatraz is in ruins. Perfect."

Mike had long since stopped laughing and had sobered. "Our stuff," he lamented. "It's going to be ruined! Your radio! My guitar!"

"Take heart," announced Rudy dramatically, "for your guitar has been located. And she's seaworthy. Look."

Mike stared. A rainbow swept in a great colorful arc across Algonkian Island. The flood waters had begun to recede and an assortment of books, clothing, baggage and sports equipment bobbed on the surface, floating out to the lake. Amid the debris floated Mike's guitar, its polished wood gleaming in the sunlight. Atop it perched the beaver, squinting around nervously.

"My guitar!" exclaimed Mike.

"Don't complain," said Rudy. "That beaver needs it more than you do. Besides, we owe him something. I have a feeling he's the guy who finished the dam we started."

"I hope the salvage crew picks it up," said Mike. A group of counsellors, led by Ralph and Jack, had stationed themselves down by the dock and were rescuing Algonkian belongings before they slipped away into the lake.

"Attention, everybody," announced Frank. "We're going to serve an impromptu supper because the day— uh—lasted longer than we expected it to."

There was a laugh from the parents and a cheer from the campers.

Frank grinned sheepishly. "Mr. Warden will be joining us later, as soon as we can get him out of his attic."

This time the laughter was general, and Frank joined it.

"Are we going to spend the night here?" asked Jeffrey hopefully.

"Oh, no," Frank assured him. "It was just a flash flood. The water's going down and we'll be able to ferry you to the mainland pretty soon."

"Darn," said Jeffrey. "I like it here."

* * *

"And so," said Arthur Warden at eight o'clock that

evening as the first group of parents prepared to board the launch, "another successful Parents' Visiting Day draws to a close."

"What does he mean 'successful'?" growled Chip to Frank.

"That's just his end of visiting day speech," grinned Frank. "He only has one, and it doesn't cover floods."

Except for the occasional puddle, all the water was gone, though the ground was still very muddy.

"Thank you for coming to Camp Algonkian Island," went on Mr. Warden. "I trust you had a nice day. Goodbye, all."

"Don't worry, folks," Frank called out to the parents, "we're okay here. In a couple of days Algonkian will be all dried out and as good as new. Goodbye, everybody."

The Millers and the Websters were gathered in a small group talking with their sons.

"Rudy," began Mrs. Miller slowly, "from all your letters and your general attitude, your father and I aren't sure that you're happy here. We've decided to ask if you'd like to come home with us now."

Chip, who had been diligently eavesdropping close by, craned his neck to catch Rudy's answer.

Rudy stared at his mother, then at Mike, and then back at his mother. It all hit him like a load of bricks. Home? There was no Mike at home, no Harold Greene, no tales of Elias, no clones. There was nothing to do at home except to entertain a pesty little brother. Alcatraz had floods and beavers and irate cooks and bow-legged camp directors and Chip throwing himself into the lake all the time ... Why would anyone want to leave such obvious entertainment just to go home?

"Heck, no," he said, eyes gleaming. "I don't want to go home. They need me here. You heard the guidance department. It's good for me. I'm staying put."

Chip burst onto the scene. "Welcome to camp, Miller! This is just great!" He clapped his big hands onto Rudy's shoulders.

"Yeah!" squeaked Mike, barely audibly.

Rudy wriggled out of Chip's grasp. "There is no need," he said blandly, "to become hysterical."

Chip laughed. Miller hadn't changed.

After all goodbyes had been said and the launch had left on its last trip, marking the end of an eventful visiting day, Rudy and Mike seated themselves on a very wet bench in the centre of the compound.

"Well?" said Mike expectantly. "Tell me. Why did you decide to stay?"

"Simple," said Rudy. "I haven't escaped yet."

"*What?*"

"You don't think I'm going to admit that Chip and Frank and all those clones kept me here?" replied Rudy. His eyes gleamed diabolically. "Now that they think I'm here to stay, it should be easy to catch them off guard. You coming?"

"But," Mike protested hoarsely. "What if we get away?"

Rudy shrugged. "Then we score ourselves a point, come back and try again."

Mike stared at him and then collapsed in a fit of helpless laughter.

14
You come back here!

It was the last day of camp. The boys of Camp Algonkian Island were lined up at the dock, their luggage beside them, waiting for their turn to board the launch that would take them to the mainland. From there, buses were waiting to take them home.

"Well," said Pierre to Chip, Frank and a group of other counsellors, "so ends the most amazing term in the history of this camp."

"And all because of one guy," added Chip. "I've never worked so hard in my life! In the last two weeks that kid has escaped nine times! We caught him six, and three he came back on his own. And for what? He didn't want to go home."

"The glory of the chase," said Pierre. "I told you Miller was a remarkable kid."

"He certainly is," purred Jack Tyler. "Algonkian Island, soccer champions of Ontario. It has a nice ring to it."

Frank sighed. "The memory of Rudy Miller with Mike Webster at his side is going to haunt us all for years."

Dave chuckled in amusement. "I'll never forget how

we took him to that track meet on the mainland and he won the hundred-metre dash and kept on running."

"We won, though," grinned Chip, "after we found him and dragged him back."

"He kept us well paid, you know," put in Pierre thoughtfully. "We'd chase him all over the place and in return he'd win us a game or a track meet once in a while."

"Speak of the devil," laughed Frank. "Here come Miller and company now."

Rudy and Mike approached and shook hands all around.

"So long, Miller," said Frank. "It's been—interesting."

"Goodbye, everybody, and thanks," said Mike.

"Yeah, so long, everybody," said Rudy. He came face to face with Chip and smiled for the second time in a month. "'Bye, Chip," he said sweetly. "See you again next year."

Then he and Mike turned and ran off towards the waiting launch.

Chip held his head. "Next year! Next year! Let's not let him in!"

Pierre laughed. "Then you'd have him breaking in instead of breaking out."

"Hey," said Frank, "here comes the supply boat with a big load. I don't remember anything being ordered. Let's see what they've got."

The launch pulled out just as the supply boat arrived at the loading dock. Frank and the group went to meet it.

"Hi. What have you got for us?" called Frank.

The delivery man produced his cargo ticket and

stood scratching his head. "Volleyballs," he said. "A thousand volleyballs."

"Who ordered *those*?" asked Chip in disbelief.

"It says here *R. Miller, Camp Director*."

"Oh, no!" moaned Frank, his face gray. "I forgot! I forgot to call back and cancel that order!"

Chip gazed at the now distant launch carrying Rudy, Mike and the other boys to the mainland. He ran to the end of the dock, waving his arms wildly.

"*Miller! You come back here!*"

About the Author

Gordon Korman wrote his first book, *This Can't Be Happening at Macdonald Hall,* as a seventh grade English project. By the time Korman had graduated from high school he had written and published five other books including *Go Jump in the Pool!, Beware the Fish!,* and *The War with Mr. Wizzle* all available in Apple Paperback editions from Scholastic Inc. He divides his time between New York City and Toronto.

APPLE® PAPERBACKS

Pick an Apple and Polish Off Some Great Reading!

NEW APPLE TITLES

☐ MT43356-3	Family Picture	Dean Hughes	$2.75
☐ MT41682-0	Dear Dad, Love Laurie	Susan Beth Pfeffer	$2.75
☐ MT41529-8	My Sister, the Creep		
	Candice F. Ransom (May '90)		$2.75

BESTSELLING APPLE TITLES

☐ MT42709-1	Christina's Ghost	Betty Ren Wright	$2.75
☐ MT43461-6	The Dollhouse Murders	Betty Ren Wright	$2.75
☐ MT42319-3	The Friendship Pact	Susan Beth Pfeffer	$2.75
☐ MT43444-6	Ghosts Beneath Our Feet	Betty Ren Wright	$2.75
☐ MT40605-1	Help! I'm a Prisoner in the Library	Eth Clifford	$2.50
☐ MT42193-X	Leah's Song	Eth Clifford	$2.50
☐ MT43618-X	Me and Katie (The Pest)	Ann M. Martin	$2.75
☐ MT42883-7	Sixth Grade Can Really Kill You	Barthe DeClements	$2.75
☐ MT40409-1	Sixth Grade Secrets	Louis Sachar	$2.75
☐ MT42882-9	Sixth Grade Sleepover	Eve Bunting	$2.75
☐ MT41732-0	Too Many Murphys		
	Colleen O'Shaughnessy McKenna		$2.75
☐ MT41118-7	Tough-Luck Karen	Johanna Hurwitz	$2.50
☐ MT42326-6	Veronica the Show-off	Nancy K. Robinson	$2.75

Available wherever you buy books...or use the coupon below.

Scholastic Inc., P.O. Box 7502, 2932 East McCarty Street, Jefferson City, MO 65102

Please send me the books I have checked above. I am enclosing $_____ (please add $2.00 to cover shipping and handling). Send check or money order — no cash or C.O.D. s please.

Name_____

Address_____

City _____ State/Zip _____

Please allow four to six weeks for delivery. Offer good in the U.S.A. only.
Sorry, mail orders are not available to residents of Canada. Prices subject to change.

APP1089